IEE MONOGRAPH SERIES 1

TECHNIQUES OF PULSE-CODE MODULATION IN COMMUNICATION NETWORKS

G. C. HARTLEY   P. MORNET   F. RALPH   D. J. TARRAN

TECHNIQUES OF
PULSE-CODE MODULATION
IN COMMUNICATION NETWORKS

CAMBRIDGE AT THE UNIVERSITY PRESS 1967

Published in association with
THE INSTITUTION OF ELECTRICAL ENGINEERS

Published by the Syndics of the Cambridge University Press
Bentley House, 200 Euston Road, London N.W. 1
American Branch: 32 East 57th Street, New York, N.Y. 10022

© The Institution of Electrical Engineers 1967

Library of Congress Catalogue Card Number: 67–15307

Printed in Great Britain
at the University Printing House, Cambridge
(Brooke Crutchley, University Printer)

CONTENTS

FOREWORD

Although the idea of pulse-code modulation was put forward 25 years ago, it is only recently that there has been a revival of interest in its potentialities as the most economic way of achieving multiple transmission of voice signals over relatively short distances on physical circuits. Wider interest in it is now developing in its application to networks in which the digital mode is maintained during switching as well as in transmission links, which could lead to a great increase in the capacity of telephone networks for handling digital data signals.

The book surveys the potentialities of pulse-code modulation and the issues involved in its adoption in communication networks, although, in a rapidly changing subject such as p.c.m., it is, of course, unavoidable that in one or two places the present state of the art has advanced beyond what is implied in the text. It is aimed at the practising engineer and graduate student seeking to broaden his knowledge of the technique.

ACKNOWLEDGMENTS

The authors wish to acknowledge the assistance given in preparing this monograph by numerous colleagues in both Laboratoire Central de Télécommunications, Paris, France, and Standard Telecommunication Laboratories, Harlow, England. In particular, they would like to mention Mr K. W. Cattermole, who provided much constructive criticism of the original draft.

1 INTRODUCTION

The idea of transmitting continuous or analogue functions such as speech by purely digital signals was first suggested many years ago (see Chapter 2), but it is only in recent years, with the development of semiconductor devices, that the application of digital techniques to systems within civil telecommunication networks has become an economic possibility. Commercial application of pulse-code-modulation (p.c.m.) systems to the alleviation of circuit shortage in the junction-network sphere has already become established practice in the USA (Fultz and Penick, 1965) and interest in similar trends can be noted in other parts of the world. In addition, international bodies such as the CCITT are now studying p.c.m. closely (CCITT, 1964a and EARC, 1963).

In the field of switching, similar pulse techniques have been investigated in application to electronic-switching exchanges, and the natural corollary has been to start considering the integration of transmission and switching, so that signals are retained in the digital form throughout the network. It is also certain that more and more information other than speech will need to be transmitted over communication networks in the future, and the integration of these types of digital signal with those arising from speech is also coming under active study.

For all of these applications, p.c.m. appears to provide an elegant solution, albeit with some attendant problems, such as the formidable one associated with synchronisation of large all-digital switched networks. It is therefore the aim of this monograph to review many of the facets of p.c.m. techniques, covering the latest developments and thinking particularly in the sphere of integrated networks. In order to render the monograph a coherent whole, a brief resumé will first be given of the historical development and of the underlying principles of p.c.m.

2 HISTORICAL REVIEW

The first multiplex telephone systems using open-wire, cable and radio-link bearers were all based on the frequency-division-multiplex (f.d.m.) principle; and the majority of the channels in the world's various telephone networks are still so derived at the present time. The cost of the channel filters required to maintain an economic 4 kc/s spacing between channels with f.d.m., however, is high; and, since wider spacings do not generally provide a more economic solution, attention has been directed to different multiplexing principles. Attention has also been directed, of course, towards cheapening conventional f.d.m. channel filters (e.g. by adopting electromechanical designs), but this is outside the scope of this monograph.

Time-division multiplex (t.d.m.), which had been used, in fact, for the Baudot telegraph system, even before the invention of the telephone, was seen to have great value. The idea of replacing the audio output from a microphone by pulse signals (pulse-width modulation, in fact) was first tried in 1924 (Heising, 1924), to improve the efficiency of a radio transmitter. However, pulse operation for a single channel does not achieve any really worthwhile economies; and, in the early 1930s (Deloraine and Reeves, 1938), the idea of multiplexing telephone channels by interleaving pulses obtained by the cyclic sampling of the various speech signals corresponding to each of these channels was conceived, and several experimental systems were constructed. However, in all these systems, the information transmitted was directly related to a characteristic of the message signal by variation of the amplitude (p.a.m.), width (p.w.m.) or position (p.p.m. or p.t.m.) of the pulse. Consequently, the disturbances inherent in the various systems of transmission (e.g. distortion, noise and crosstalk) could still considerably affect the received signal, just as in the case of the analogue f.d.m. system, even though it is admitted that all

2

forms of pulse operation achieve some signal/noise-ratio advantage in exchange for increased bandwidth.

This led to the idea of quantisation, which, in essence, is the acceptance of a certain minimum signal/noise ratio. Then, to avoid the deleterious effects of transmission disturbances, it was necessary to regenerate the pulses before the stage had been reached where the disturbances could cause ambiguity between the quanta—a process which had been known and exploited by telegraph engineers for many years, using binary signals. This, in turn, called for some form of coding of the speech message, to produce telegraph-like signals, and it was such a system (i.e. p.c.m.) that Reeves invented and patented in 1938 (Reeves, 1938).

The underlying principles of p.c.m. are given in Chapter 3; but it basically consists in the transmission of numbers representing the amplitude measurements of samples taken regularly from the speech signals. Thus, the information lies only in the presence or absence of the code pulses, and it is, to a certain extent, independent of their amplitude, width and phase.

P.C.M. was invented mainly for line-of-sight microwave links, where the extra bandwidth required was then readily available. In fact, however, the first commercial applications (Fultz and Penick, 1965) (i.e. disregarding military systems) were to junction-area cable systems, where compatibility problems did not arise, rather than to toll or trunk routes, where conventional systems would have to interconnect.

Since the Second World War, there has been a growing emphasis on p.c.m. studies in many countries—an emphasis given a considerable stimulus after about 1954, with the advent of practical semiconductors. Among the features covered have been:

(i) the examination of numerous techniques of coding

(ii) the investigation of p.c.m. television transmission over long-haul waveguides (Neu, 1960)

(iii) the propounding of other digit-coding systems such as delta modulation (Deloraine *et al.*, 1946) and log-differential p.c.m. (Cutler, 1950)

(iv) the application of p.c.m. to long-haul radio links, with a view to using the signal/noise advantage to permit more frequent use of the radio frequencies in a given band (EARC, 1963)

(v) the use of small-capacity p.c.m. radio links for short-haul application in the 11 Gc/s band.

All these aspects will be covered more fully in later Chapters.

3 PRINCIPLES OF P.C.M.

This Chapter is divided into six main sections. The first of these gives a fairly elementary outline of the basic underlying principles for the benefit of those new to p.c.m., and it can accordingly be omitted by any who are already familiar with the subject. The second deals with the main transmission and multiplexing features, as well as dealing briefly with transmission applications to various media. The third covers the various features peculiar to switching in the p.c.m. mode; and, in particular, it outlines the methods of synchronous and quasisynchronous integrated-network operation. The fourth and fifth deal with the chief pros and cons of p.c.m. and the performance features, respectively; while the last introduces the other two digital modes of single-digit and log-differential p.c.m.

3.1 Basic concepts

3.1.1 Time sampling

Consider first a speech waveform such as might be represented by Fig. 1. In this diagram, ordinate lines have been drawn at regular time intervals, so that they represent the instantaneous values of the speech wave at a sequence of instants. A device which produces a series of very short pulses of current or voltage, so that the amplitudes of the pulses exactly represent the characteristic ordinates in the speech wave (i.e. the output is amplitude-modulated pulses, or p.a.m.), is said to be a time-sampling device. Fig. 2 indicates one form which such a device may take. The speech-wave source s is applied to a low-pass filter (to limit the frequency band, as explained in the next paragraph) terminated in a resistance r. By means of appropriate timing pulses, the gate G permits the instantaneous voltage across r to be transferred to the input terminals of the amplifier A, which is assumed to have a high input impedance. An appropriate series of time-scale pulses are then obtained across the output load resistance R of A.

In any physically realisable transmission system, the message or modulating function has the major part of the energy limited to a finite frequency band. Orthodox sampling theory, which is based on

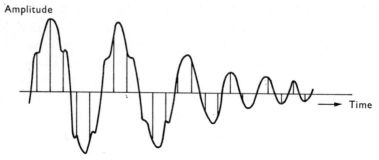

Fig. 1   Time-sampled speech waveform

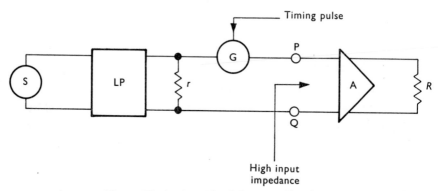

Fig. 2   Block schematic of time-sampling device

an ideal limited frequency band, can therefore be applied reasonably safely to the practical case. This theory states that, if the highest frequency component is f_c cycles per second, the time function of the message cannot assume more than $2f_c$ independent values per second. For this reason, the amplitudes at any set of points t seconds apart, where $t = 1/2f_c$, completely specify the message. Thus, to transmit an ideal band-limited message of duration T, it is sufficient merely to

6

send the $2f_cT$ independent values obtained by sampling the instantaneous amplitude of the signal at a regular rate of $2f_c$ samples per second.

Fig. 3 shows the spectrum of the sampled message developed in the load resistance R of Fig. 2, for the case where the sampling frequency f_s is greater than $2f_c$. It will be seen that the signals consist, in fact, of the original speech signal B plus a series of components which fall into discrete families consisting of either the sampling frequency or one of its harmonics, together with upper- and lower-sideband signals located above and below the appropriate harmonic of the sampling frequency. The magnitudes of the harmonics and sideband components diminish with frequency, and they are dependent upon the width (i.e. time duration) of the pulse in the load resistance R.

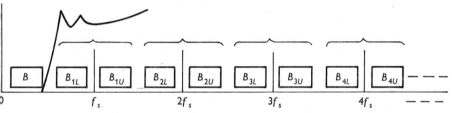

Fig. 3   Spectrum of time-sampled signal

Reverting to Fig. 2, it will be clear that if, across points P and Q, a second circuit is connected, identical to that shown to the left of PQ and supplied with timing pulses of exactly the same frequency as before but slightly displaced in time, it is possible to transmit speech from this second circuit as time-sampled pulses into amplifier A. If, at the receiving end of the circuit, similar gates are employed to direct pulses into the correct low-pass filters, an additional channel will have been added to the system. There is clearly no theoretical limit to the number of channels which may be so added, provided that their pulses are uniformly and discretely spaced on the time scale. There will, of course, be a practical limit arising from the limitations of gating techniques.

The block schematic of Fig. 2, which could, of course, be arranged to transmit pulses of one sign only, by introducing a bias voltage in

7

series with the output of amplifier A, so that the transmitted pulses vary in amplitude but not in sign, according to the speech input signal, produces p.a.m./t.d.m. signals.

3.1.2 Signal reconstruction

If the series of pulses derived by time-sampling can be accurately transmitted to a distant point, it is easily seen from Fig. 3 that the original speech signal may be recovered by the simple process of inserting a low-pass filter to accept the band B. It can also be mentioned, in passing, that recovery of the original signal can also be achieved by means of bandpass filters picking off sidebands, either single or double. The method of detection will then depend on whether the harmonic of the sampling frequency is present or not. This feature, however, is not of great practical interest.

A further important point is evident by inspection of Fig. 3; namely, the reason why the sampling frequency f_s must be at least twice the maximum signal frequency. If this is not the case, the lower sideband (shown as B_{1L}) and the original voiceband B will overlap each other, and it will no longer be possible to extract undistorted speech signals. In practice, a gap must be allowed between these two bands, to ensure that a practical filter can adequately pass the speech-band while sufficiently suppressing all other signals. Such a filter characteristic is shown superimposed on Fig. 3.

3.1.3 Quantisation

The processes discussed so far have produced pulse-amplitude-modulated (p.a.m.) pulses. However, p.a.m. is unsuited for transmission over long distances, owing to the difficulty of correcting with sufficient accuracy for the variation of line attenuation and phase shift with frequency. Quite small errors will result in a change in the shape of the received pulse, which, in a t.d.m. system, results in crosstalk, thus rendering the system unusable. If, however, only certain discrete amplitudes of sample size are permitted, so that, when the message is sampled, the amplitude nearest to the true amplitude is sent; provided that the received signal is not excessively altered by line

8

noise and distortion from that transmitted, it is possible to determine accurately which discrete amplitude the signal is supposed to have. Thus the signal can be reformed, or a new signal created, which has the amplitude originally sent.

Representing the message in this manner, by allowing only certain discrete amplitudes, is called quantising. The process of measurement is illustrated in Fig. 4, in which the series of lines equidistant from each other on each side of the centre line AB represent the scale of (for example) voltage against which each pulse will be measured.

Quantisation inherently introduces an initial error in the amplitude of the samples, giving rise to quantisation distortion. One important property of this error is evident from examination of Fig. 4. This is that, whatever the amplitude of the pulse, the magnitude of the error voltage will be determined, on average, by the degree of separation of the level lines; so that the average

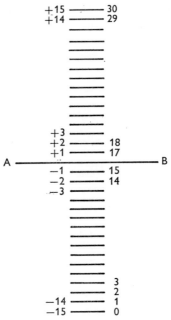

Fig. 4   Linear quantising levels

quantising-error power associated with the reproduced signal will be independent of the magnitude of the signal itself.

This error power can be made as small as desired by placing the level lines closer together; but, when it is remembered that the system may be required to handle speech volumes varying over a range of perhaps 35–40 dB, it will be obvious that, if the level lines are placed very close together, in order to make the quantising error power acceptably small when small signal levels are being transmitted, the total number of levels required to transmit the largest signals could be very large indeed.

3.1.4 Instantaneous companding

Since the quantising-error power is present as noise only when the speech itself is present, a satisfactory subjective result can be obtained if the ratio of signal power to quantising-error power is maintained constant with varying signal levels. A system of quantising

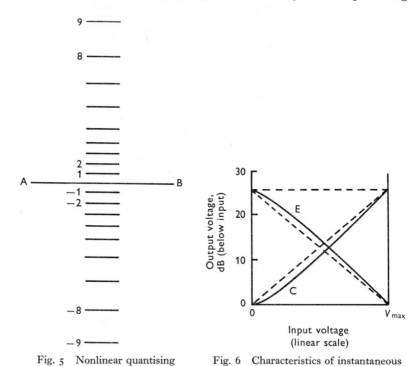

Fig. 5   Nonlinear quantising levels

Fig. 6   Characteristics of instantaneous compressor and expander

levels such as that indicated in Fig. 5, in which the intervals (or quanta) between adjacent levels gradually increase as the level itself increases, would tend to make the ratio of signal to quantising-distortion power more nearly constant.

With an approximately logarithmic law governing the increase in quantum size, it is possible to obtain an approximately constant ratio of instantaneous signal to quantising-error power over a wide range of speech volumes, while at the same time employing much fewer levels than would be required in the linear case. A truly logarithmic characteristic down to zero amplitude would require an infinite number of steps; so that, in practice, it is usual to adopt a characteristic which approximates to logarithmic at large amplitudes, and to linear at low amplitudes.

In practical systems, this result can be achieved either by direct instrumentation of nonlinear quantisation (logarithmic, hyperbolic and multilinear segments are all feasible) applied to the encoding process (see Section 3.1.5) or by using a linear quantiser, as in Fig. 4, in conjunction with a device immediately before it which introduces increasing loss as the level of the pulse applied to it increases. Such a device is known as a compressor, and, in practice, it would have a characteristic somewhat similar to curve C in Fig. 6.

Since the compressor acts on the instantaneous value of the applied short-pulse signal, it is termed an instantaneous compressor, to distinguish it from the other type of slow-acting compressor (the syllabic compressor), where the time constants are such that the device acts on the average signal power over the duration of a syllable.

Of course, there must be a device at the receiving end with a complementary characteristic, in order to restore all pulses to their correct relative level. This device will therefore present a high loss to low-level pulses, and a gradually diminishing loss as the level increases. Such a characteristic is indicated by curve E in Fig. 6. This type of device is called an expander, and the combined operation of the compressor and expander is usually known as companding. It will be evident that, in order to avoid overall distortion, it is necessary that the expander characteristic should match that of the compressor very accurately.

3.1.5 Coding

A quantised sample could be sent as a single pulse having, for example, certain possible discrete amplitudes. However, since many sample amplitudes are required (of the order of 100 for speech) it would be difficult to make circuits able to distinguish one from another. On the other hand, it is easy to make a circuit able to determine whether a pulse is present or not. To maintain the required 100 or so levels, the number of such on/off pulses required to represent each sample amplitude must therefore be increased. In general, a code group of n pulses of b possible discrete amplitudes can be used to represent b^n signal amplitudes. For the usual p.c.m. case of on/off pulses, b is 2, and the code is known as binary or base-2 code. Other codes are possible where $b = 3$ (ternary) or 4 (quaternary) etc., but the principal emphasis is on binary developments. This may not remain true if, and when, p.c.m. transmission comes to be considered for application to the long-haul analogue network, where the high inherent signal/noise ratio may make the choice of a radix higher than 2 attractive.

Practical systems employing companding, as discussed in Section 3.1.4, need about seven binary digits (i.e. equivalent to 128 levels) to adequately handle the range of speech levels encountered in practice (compared with about 11 digits required for linear quantising). Such a group of binary digits or bits employed to represent each speech sample is called a character.

Practical systems also need to take account of the difficulties incurred with unrestricted sequences of binary signals which can give rise to long sequences of either marks or spaces. Such signals will not be faithfully transmitted by a transmission medium with a low-frequency cutoff (e.g. a repeatered cable), and they are also devoid of the timing information essential to the regenerator (see Section 3.2). One method of dealing with this problem is to adopt a modified code which restricts the repertoire of binary-digit sequences to those most easily transmissible, e.g. low-disparity codes (Cattermole, 1964). Another is to adopt what is, in effect, ternary transmission, by inverting alternate mark signals (Aaron, 1962). These points are dealt with more fully in Sections 3.2.1 and 6.2.1.

In general, the coding of a p.a.m./t.d.m. group of channels (e.g. the 24 channels of a typical junction carrier system) is carried out in a single common coder, working, of course, n times as fast as for a single channel, where n is the number of channels multiplexed. The output from such a coder, obtained by sampling each channel once, is termed a frame. The pulse pattern, or multiplex structure, likely to be found in such a frame is discussed in Section 3.2.3.

3.1.6 Decoding

Decoding of a binary pulse train is obviously the reverse of the encoding process, and it involves generating a pulse which is the linear sum of the pulses in a received code group, each multiplied by its place value in that group (i.e. by 1, b, b^2, b^3 etc.). There are basically two different ways of doing this; namely, either by accumulating the received information in a digital memory and decoding all in one step, or by decoding each element of information as it arrives and integrating the code signal in an analogue store. The latter method tends to give larger errors, and all practical systems use digital memories.

3.2 Transmission and multiplexing

3.2.1 Line transmission over paired cable

The line-transmission problem of p.c.m. is basically that of creating a high-speed digital-transmission capability, and this may be achieved in different ways on different media. It has already been indicated that it is required, in general, to be able to make use of regeneration to increase bandwidth at the cost of signal/noise ratio on the line itself. This can be accomplished most simply on paired cable; and, as this is the medium involved in all current applications, it will be described first.

The problem is essentially that of transmitting a very high-speed isochronous d.c. telegraph signal, substantially without error, over a cable pair. To reduce crosstalk, balanced transmission is needed, and the problems of power feed to regenerators make interposed transformers necessary; so that the type of signal normally used is substantially that of double-current telegraph. The pulses sent to line from the transmitting terminal will be substantially square pulses, in general; i.e. the rise time and decay time will constitute only a

13

small fraction of the time unit allocated to the pulses. After transmission over a length of line, however, the pulses will become modified in shape, owing to the line characteristics; and if, after a given length of line, an equaliser and amplifier are inserted with a view to restoring them to their original shape, they will, in a practical system, appear rather as indicated in Fig. 7, where the rounding off arises primarily from a deliberate limitation of the transmitted bandwidth to something approaching the theoretical minimum.

Since, with such a system, the shape of the original pulse is known in any case, it is possible to employ a device, at repeater points, which first determines for each time interval which sign of pulse has been received, and then transmits to line a new pulse of optimum shape for the particular conditions.

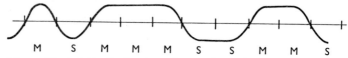

M   S   M   M   M   S   S   M   M   S

Fig. 7   Typical idealised pulse-train waveform after transmission over length of line

In a practical case, owing to the effects of external interference and imperfect transmission characteristics, the received pulses will not have the convenient shape suggested by Fig. 7. A further factor also contributing to their distortion is that, whereas the line system should theoretically transmit down to zero frequency, this is not really practicable (e.g. owing to the presence of power-separating filters). In practice, it is convenient, and possible, to avoid zero-frequency transmission, although some distortion of pulses does result from this.

The effects of noise and other distortion will be minimised if the decision regarding which sign of pulse is received is taken by examining the incoming pulse for a period at about the middle of the appropriate time interval which it occupies (see also Section 6.2.2). Fig. 8 illustrates, in principle, a method of doing this. After passing through an equaliser and amplifier, the signals reach gates G, which, by means of suitable timing pulses, are open for a very short period at about the centre of each unit time interval. Connected to the output of the gates is a flip-flop, which receives any spiked pulses that pass through the gate. Any of these which have a sufficient amplitude cause the flip-flop to transmit a completely new pulse to line. Signals less than this amplitude are unable to operate the flip-flop, which will remain in its previous position.

It will be evident that, as long as the signal has not been allowed to deteriorate at the input of the repeater unit to such an extent that it is not possible to determine with very high certainty which sign of pulse is received, the repeater device in Fig. 8 will theoretically

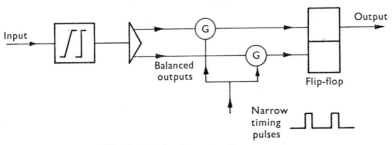

Fig. 8   Block schematic of regenerator

remove completely all the adverse effects that the signal has suffered during its passage through the previous line section; and this process may be repeated as frequently as desired, until the end of the line is reached. Such repeatering is known as regeneration, and the actual repeaters are known as regenerators.

Ideally, therefore, the signals reproduced at the far end may be made completely independent of the degradations affecting them along the route, provided that, at no point, are such degradations allowed to exceed certain limits. This is one of the most important characteristics of p.c.m. systems. In practice, the problems associated with timing the regeneration process place a limit on the degree of perfection that can be achieved.

In Fig. 8, a source of timing pulses was assumed, without considering how it might be obtained. In practice, the necessary timing information is obtained from the received signals themselves, as discussed in further detail in Section 6.2.2. Fig. 9 shows one example of a simplified schematic development of Fig. 8, involving such timing-extraction equipment. Nevertheless, however sophisticated the circuits for deriving the timing pulses are, and although these pulses will, on average, have the correct frequency, they may nevertheless be displaced slightly (either advanced or retarded) in time from their correct mean position. The new pulses transmitted by the repeater will therefore also be subjected to this time displacement (usually described as 'timing jitter'), and this effect may be cumulative as the signals pass through many repeaters; and so it is thus a function of the total route length. This possibility of cumulative jitter is an important factor in regenerative-repeater design.

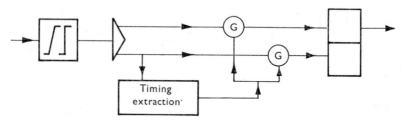

Fig. 9   Block schematic of the method of extracting the timing wave

The speed limitation imposed by this mode of transmission arises from the need to limit the attenuation in a section to a value which will still provide a possibility of detection at the regenerator, with an adequate degree of freedom from error in the face of external interference. With both outward and return directions in the same cable, one of the most likely sources of interference in the spectrum concerned is near-end crosstalk from another system. This, of course, cannot be countered by increase in transmitted power. With regenerator spacing dictated, in practice, by that of the loading coils which they replace (i.e. usually 2000 yd apart), the comfortable limit is in the region of 1·5 Mbit/s. Such an order of bit speed is developed by all the present-day p.c.m. junction carrier systems (e.g. 24 channels with 8 kc/s sampling and 8 bit/character yields 1·536 Mbit/s). In practice, the need to control the falloff in transmission efficiency in the neighbourhood of the bit frequency means that frequencies in excess of 750 kc/s have to be transmitted. This is discussed further in Section 6.2.2.

This type of regenerated digital transmission in its simple binary form imposes restraints on the nature of the transmitted intelligence. It must contain no sustained d.c. component, and, indeed, it should not contain significant low-frequency components (i.e. components ten octaves, say, below the basic bit rate), since these will cause distortion beyond the possibility of equalisation and they will degrade the reliability of the system to the ultimate point of total failure.

This may be countered by the use of special code structures— so-called low-disparity codes (Cattermole, 1964); but an alternative approach has been used, in which the line signals are, in effect, ternary, i.e. the transmitter has three conditions—positive, negative and zero (Aaron, 1962). Zero is used to transmit 'space', and positive and negative pulses are used alternately to transmit marks. This system is completely free from direct current, but it is inevitably more sensitive to noise, since the detector has to distinguish between three states and not two. This type of transmission is known as bipolar or alternate-mark inversion (a.m.i.). Both straight binary systems and alternate-mark-inversion systems demand a sufficient number of reversals to ensure 'clock extraction' without significant phase wander. The pros and cons of the two systems are discussed in more detail in Section 6.2.1.

Some aspects of multiplex structures suitable for a binary transmission line are examined in Section 3.2.3.

3.2.2 Transmission over other media

Coaxial cables

The deloaded cable pair is the main basis for contemporary application, because the incentive is to extract more use out of existing cable plant. However, application on a wide scale, particularly (but not solely) if this is associated with some increase in length of route, is very likely to bring about early examination of coaxial cable. In general, the problems of this medium would be similar to those of the paired cable, except that attenuation would be lower and cross-talk would also be less; so that considerably higher bit rates would be feasible. It does not follow, however, that the optimum solution would be the same. Improved noise standards and possibilities of more accurate equalising could make it attractive to employ equalised amplifiers for several consecutive sections, before it became necessary to have recourse to regeneration. The inherently high signal/noise ratio of the medium could also be economically traded for a system using a radix higher than 2.

There seems little doubt that small-core coaxial cable can be very satisfactorily arranged to handle the order of 1000 channels; and the limiting factor (particularly with large-core cable) may well be, for some time, the instrumentation difficulties in terminals and repeaters rather than any theoretical limitations due to noise and bandwidth considerations. Nevertheless, the exploitation of this medium seems very likely as soon as the scale of usage makes its channel capacity attractive.

Submarine cable

This is a special case of the coaxial problem already referred to. Its high-quality construction and stable environment provide ideal transmission conditions. Digital cable could be constructed at an early date, with an adequate speed capacity; but the economics of transferring large quantities of voice traffic to this mode is still debatable. Military digital systems, however, have already been tested (King *et al.*, 1961).

On the other hand, the high performance standards of existing cable open the way to multilevel audio modulation, providing a capacity for some digital handling, e.g. transmitting data which, in the tributary area, have been integrated with p.c.m. speech (see Sections 4.2 and 5.1.5). Schemes have been proposed using a radix of 8 to provide a capability of 960 kbit/s for the 404 kc/s bandwidth of a TAT3-type system, or a capability of 2·8 Mbit/s for the 1·1 Mc/s bandwidth required for a 270, 4 kc/s-channel f.d.m. system.

Radio links

While, at first sight, it might be expected that the wide use of frequency bandwidth entailed with p.c.m. techniques would be undesirable, since the immense latent bandwidth of an enclosed medium simply is not there; there are, however, compensating considerations, and certain workers (particularly the Japanese)* have claimed attractive possibilities for economic application in the trunk network. The principal compensations are:

(a) The easement of requirements for extreme linearity and freedom from intermodulation make available a greater portion of the nominal bandwidth of the system, and hence compensate somewhat for the greater bandwidth required for the p.c.m. mode.

(b) The reduced crosstalk demands make repeated use of the same radio frequencies far easier; so that frequency allocation is less restrictive.

Against these advantages must be set the need for more conservative route planning, to achieve larger fading margins than with conventional f.m. radio links, since fades in excess of the planned margin could produce complete failure (rather than performance deterioration) in the p.c.m. case.

The overall result of these conflicting restraints is that, in spite of the reduced number of telephone channels obtainable on any one route with a particular r.f. carrier, the permissible increased reuse of the same r.f. carrier in a given area does, in fact, allow the total traffic capacity to be increased. This can be of immense benefit in a densely populated country with large and growing traffic demands, although it is by no means certain that the p.c.m. solution is the optimum where the r.f. allocation problems are less pressing.

There is growing interest in small-capacity (24-, 48- or 96-channel) p.c.m. radio links operating in the 11 Gc/s band for short-haul applications, e.g. city centre to periphery.

Satellites

In this relatively new branch of the communication art, the study of the multiaccess problem has not yet shown that any one modulation method has overriding advantages over any other. The first commercial applications have adopted the f.d.m./f.m. mode, but the amount of multiaccess capability has been strictly limited. In the

* *NEC News*, Dec. 1963

military case, however, the broadcast nature of the satellite transmission necessitates the use of encryption, and, as will be explained in Section 4.1, p.c.m. proves very attractive in this application.

The multiaccess facility gives rise to synchronisation difficulties, and these difficulties are, of course, magnified when the satellite is a moving one. One solution that has been proposed (Campbell, 1964) entails that each ground station should, in turn, send a burst of several kilobits up into the satellite, the phasing being such that each ground station's burst arrives sequentially at the satellite. This entails the provision of guardbands between the bursts. In the satellite, the received signal would be amplified in a simple broadband analogue repeater with no severe requirements on linearity and rebroadcast generally. Each ground-station burst would contain an address signal to enable the addressee to pick out the correct bits from the total bit stream. One ground station would be arranged to transmit regularly, in order to provide a regular frame reference for synchronisation purposes.

Guided media

For media such as long-haul and optical waveguides, the unavoidable phase-distortion characteristics consequent on the many slight discontinuities imply that there is a high probability that digital transmission will prove to be the only practicable transmission method. P.C.M. transmission has already been tried experimentally for television and for 24-channel telephony over long-haul waveguides.

Looking well into the future (25 years hence, say), some workers foresee a widespread demand for closed-circuit television (e.g. for information retrieval from central processing centres), with an attendant large increase in network bandwidth required. Such bandwidth may well come from optical beams, where vast reserves are available. The efficiency of optical methods for a given signal/noise ratio is many times greater when digital, rather than analogue, methods are employed; and p.c.m. with between, say, 16 and 80 levels would meet many of the television requirements very well. Television with 81 levels over long-haul waveguide was publicly demonstrated as long ago as 1959.*

* *J. IEE*, 1959, **5**, p. 195

The key technical problem in this area is the achievement of a design of waveguide incorporating low cost and high flexibility.

3.2.3 Multiplex structures

The simplest form of digital t.d.m. that suggests itself is that of bit interleaving; i.e. a frame consisting of one bit from each contributing channel in succession. However, in the actual operations of a common coder, the process begins by examination of p.a.m. samples from the various channels in succession. These p.a.m. samples are converted into quantised samples represented by characters, and it is therefore obviously more convenient to arrange the resultant digital multiplex by interleaving complete characters, and not bits.

At the receiving end (decoder), an inverse process takes place. Characters are defined by a continuous counting process, which, however, demands the availability of an agreed starting point or frame marking. This is obtained by either adding extra bits or using the whole or part of one channel to transmit a fixed identifiable character (the pros and cons of the various methods of synchronising are discussed in Section 6.1.4). With character interleaving, the receiving end has no additional problem of defining the character, provided that it can identify this multiplex frame, to enable it to associate characters with their correct channels. In a bit-interleaved structure, this relationship is more obscure, and, although a similar capability can be created, this is only at the expense of more hardware.

This character interleaving also makes possible the easement of regeneration, by the restriction of characters to certain patterns (e.g. unit disparity), as mentioned in Section 3.2.1. In a bit-interleaved system, such manipulations may secure, in the long term, freedom from direct current, but the actual makeup of bits in any frame is not predictable.

The trend to character interleaving is therefore fairly universally accepted, and it is likely to remain so. The only coding system naturally compatible with bit interleaving is elementary delta (see Section 3.6.1), and this is unlikely to achieve the standards required. In a character system, it is immaterial from the point of view of this analysis whether the characters represent straight p.c.m. or differential p.c.m. (log delta—see Section 3.6.2).

For the purposes of signalling, it is a fairly universal practice to add a signalling bit to each character, to obtain the equivalent of an outband-signalling facility. While this provides a relatively large information capacity per channel, it does lead to simple instrumentation for two-condition signalling. For 3- or 4-condition signalling, which should cover most types of switching plant, a further stage of time division provides 2 bits at half the speed for alternate frames.

For integrated p.c.m. networks, there is a case for common channel or order-wire signalling, and this aspect is discussed further in Section 3.3.8.

3.3 Principles of p.c.m. switching

3.3.1 Introduction

The special features of p.c.m.-transmission systems are obviously much more effectively realised if complete switched networks can be established, so that the voice remains in the digital mode until it is finally decoded for connection to the subset. Further, such a process improves the overall economics by eliminating the cost of intermediate decoding and recoding operations. This reduced cost is dependent, it is true, on the actual cost of switching the digital intelligence not significantly exceeding that of switching analogue voice. Studies to date indicate that it may well be considerably less.

The following subsections discuss the general nature of the p.c.m.-switching problem and some of the alternative modes of approach now under examination. An outline of one practical design is given in Section 6.3.

3.3.2 Basic elements of a tandem switch

It is convenient to begin by examining the problems of interconnecting the channels of a number of p.c.m. multiplex links. This is the basic function of a tandem switch, and it is the foundation on which all other types of switch must be created. Fig. 10 shows the essential functions which must be executed—demultiplexing, cross-office transfer and remultiplexing. These can be executed in a variety of ways. If the incoming and outgoing multiplexes were bit-interleaved, demultiplexing would produce a channel bit stream at, say, 56 kbit/s, and this could be relayed across a substantially conventional space switch and reassembled. It would be necessary to include some form of phase-adjusting buffer.

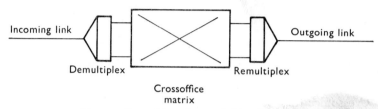

Fig. 10   Essential tandem-switching functions

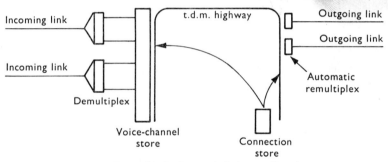

Fig. 11   Example of t.d.m. switch for small exchange

In practice, however, as has already been pointed out, most p.c.m. systems so far experimented with have adopted character inter-leaving; and while, in principle, this does not rule out space switching, time-division switching does produce a much more elegant solution. Accordingly, the current trend is towards a very close integration of demultiplexing and remultiplexing with the switching functions on a t.d.m. basis.

Fig. 11 shows the way in which this has been tackled on one experimental military design for a small exchange. A number of incoming links are demultiplexed, and the characters associated with each channel are stored in a voice-channel store with one location per channel.

23

These characters are read out under the control of a connection store with a time slot for each outgoing channel, and transferred via a common highway to stores associated with the outgoing link. The sequence of handling by this connection store is so arranged that, if the transferred characters are read out serially on each outgoing link, the outgoing multiplex is automatically reassembled. Thus, if such a switch is handling six links of 24 channels each, the sequence of transfer across the office over the common 'highway' is

Channel 1 of link 1:channel 1 of link 2:channel 1 of link 3...channel 1 of link 6:channel 2 of link 1:channel 2 of link 2...channel 24 of link 6.

Crossoffice transfer could be either on a parallel basis using multiple highways or serially on a single highway, e.g. between shift registers.

3.3.3 Application to larger switches

This elementary approach is obviously applicable only to very small units. Six or eight 24-channel systems may be interconnected by a single highway, but anything more than this leads to difficulties,

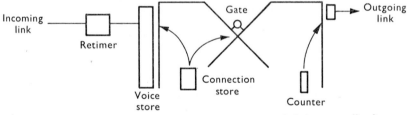

Fig. 12   Switched-highway principle for a larger switch (say 2000 lines)

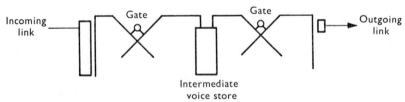

Fig. 13   Intermediate store for a very large switch

owing to the unmanageably high crossoffice speed of operation. Fig. 12 shows an obvious step of introducing several highways interconnected in the switched-highway mode already familiar in p.a.m./t.d.m. switching. If, for simplicity, the outgoing highway employs for each connection the time slot of the outgoing channel desired, there will admittedly be significant blocking. For larger switches, something like that in Fig. 13 is to be preferred. This comprises two consecutive switched-highway stages with a 'slot changing' store in between. This may be a static store, such as a high-speed magnetic store or a capacity/diode store, or a dynamic store, such as a delay line.

3.3.4 Problem of synchronisation

Before discussing crossoffice trunking in greater detail, it is necessary to examine a very fundamental underlying problem—that of synchronisation. The elementary outlines in the preceding paragraphs could depend for their realisation on complete stability of the speed and phase relationships of all incoming and outgoing digit streams. In practice, this will not be the case, for two distinct reasons:

(a) The streams may be derived from independent clocks differing slightly in speed (drift).

(b) Even if the clocks are identical, there will be phase wander and jitter, owing to temperature variations of propagation speed on the cable and in the phase response of regenerators. In a simple star network, e.g. a tandem switch and a number of dependent local exchanges, it is simple and adequate to arrange that all the transmission from local exchanges is based on a clock derived from, or locked to, the incoming bit stream. A master-clock capability is thus established. An extended network, however, involving many tandem centres, cannot be handled in this way. A literal single-master-clock concept is undesirable from many points of view, and various forms of fairly sophisticated clock correlation are being examined instead.

There is therefore, as yet, an unresolved debate on the merits of a system which is based on the identity of mean speed of all clocks (fully synchronous) and a system which arrives at the closest correlation achievable but continues to function in the face of imperfections in this correlation (quasisynchronous). This latter approach accepts, as a consequence of any speed differences, certain minor mutilations of information in transit in a manner to be described.

Retiming

Before examining these two modes (i.e. fully synchronous and quasisynchronous) in greater detail, it is desirable to examine the problem of wander and jitter referred to under (*b*) in Section 3.3.4. This is common to both modes, and experiments are being carried out with various essentially similar solutions.

Fig. 14*a* shows the principle of a retimer designed for the parallel-transfer mode. Demultiplexing takes place at a clock speed derived from the incoming bit stream and following it continuously and exactly (i.e. controlled by the phase monitor in Fig. 14*a*); the resultant channel characters are transferred to one of two or three re-timing stores per link (actually shown in Fig. 14*a* as selector levels). Whether there are two or three stores depends on whether the store is filled 'serially' from the link bit stream, or whether characters are initially staticised in the link circuit (e.g. in a shift register) and transferred in parallel. This present description will cover the latter form as being slightly simpler to deal with, although either arrangement is equally effective.

The characters stored in the retiming store are now read out (in parallel) into the voice-channel store, and this process is executed by the demultiplex control store under control of the local clock. Fig. 14*b* shows the timing of this process; it will be seen that, at the start of the period indicated (situation A), the reading out occurs approximately one character length (say, 5 μs) after the writing in. Later, a situation B is shown, in which this margin is reduced to a small fraction of a character, owing to the incoming clock gaining on the outgoing clock, and successful transfer becomes endangered. This condition may be simply detected, and when it is, the demultiplex unit 'slips' by moving over to the pattern indicated in stage C. Read-out is now once again one character after write in; but, in the slip process, one character has been completely omitted. Similarly, if the incoming clock lags behind the outgoing clock, one character is read twice, but, with destructive readout, this implies a gap at the second readout.

In a multiplex structure where one channel is devoted to a synchronisation character, it is easy to arrange that slip occurs on this character and that no user intelligence is lost at this stage.

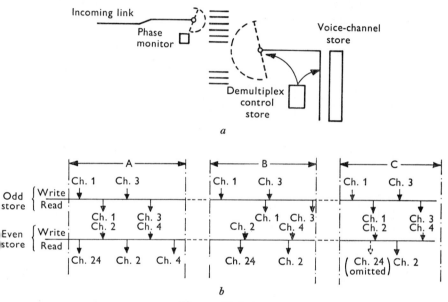

a

b

Fig. 14   Retiming
a   Principle of retimer for parallel-transfer mode
b   Operation of retiming and introduction of slip

The demultiplex control, when slip occurs, is arranged to maintain the integrity of multiplex structure; i.e. when a character is omitted and the following character is transferred instead, the controlling count is advanced by an extra step and the new character is transferred to its correct destination. The result can then be correct transfer of all characters to the voice memory; but, when slip occurs, all characters belonging to channels associated with the link in question are transferred 5 μs earlier. Similarly, when a character is read twice, the controlling count is held for one step.

Fig. 15 shows a retimer or aligner related to a serial-transfer mode. In this, the incoming digits are delivered to a static store, which may conveniently be one character long, but longer if necessary. They are then transferred to the switch by reading out from this store at a phase which is normally half of the store length behind the writing in. Delivery to the switch is then independent of wander in the incoming stream, and no mutilation will arise provided that the maximum deviation is significantly less than half the store length.

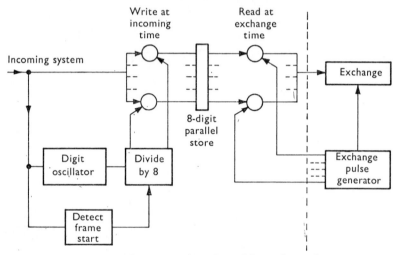

Fig. 15   Aligner or retimer for serial transfer mode

This degree of retiming, and the provision of adequate 'backlash', can be regarded as basic to any mode of approach. Differences in attitude arise, however, in relation to the problem of permanent clock drift referred to under (*a*) in Section 3.3.4, as follows.

Fully synchronous approach

If a retimer of the type indicated in Fig. 15 is applied to the case of identical or fully correlated clocks, it is now possible to interconnect incoming and outgoing links via a switch such as that shown in Fig. 13, in which the junctors comprise variable-delay cords whose function is to accept a character at time T_x from an incoming link and deliver it at time T_y to the correct outgoing link. A method in

28

which a great deal of traffic can be accommodated on zero-delay or small fixed-delay cords, by choosing T_y to be the same as T_x, has been published (Walker and Duerdoth, 1964).

It should be pointed out, perhaps, that this approach depends, not only on maintenance of a synchronised clock at all terminals and a retimer to remove transmission phase wander, but also on the retention of a predetermined frame phasing; i.e. the time slot at which the nth channel of a link is delivered to the switch must be the same for

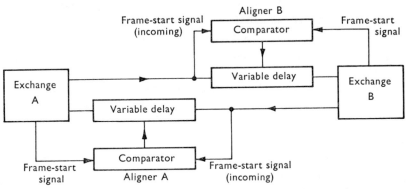

Fig. 16   Compensation of variable delay of transmission path

all links. To secure this, the sending end must relate its frame to that of the incoming direction or to some other 'system' method of frame delineation, and delay units must be included in each link to compensate for the propagation delay of the line in use. Such delay units are shown in Fig. 16.

Quasisynchronous approach

If the above measures for complete synchronisation can be realised, there is no need to store the incoming intelligence, except insofar as is needed for retiming or aligning purposes (one or two characters).

The quasisynchronous approach admits the storage of a complete frame at the input to a switch, i.e. one character per channel. Once this is done, it becomes possible to permit drift in the phasing of delivery to this input, provided that the consequence is faced that there will be occasional mutilation of the intelligence.

If Fig. 14 is examined in greater detail, it will be seen that, across the office, the characters in the voice store are now read out at intervals of $24 \times 5 = 120 \mu s$. The clock controls, however, are so arranged that writing into the voice store is on one clock phase and reading out is on another. There will come a time (ultimately every 24th slip in the retimer) when a character is written into the voice store just after, instead of just before, it is read. Only then is there any mutilation of user intelligence.

It should be noted that reassembly of all outgoing multiplexes is completely regular, and that the final result is that, in order to fit incoming information which is slightly faster or slower into this regular stream, a character has occasionally to be left out or a dummy inserted.

One would hope to achieve clock correlation to at least one part in 10^6. This, on a voice channel, means mutilation of a sample once in 125 s for an 8 kc/s sampling rate. A figure better than this by an order of magnitude may well be easily attainable (e.g. once in 21 min for 10^{-7} clock correlation or 3·47 h for 10^{-8}); but, in any case, the resultant noise is negligible, although it may be more serious for other classes of intelligence (see Section 4.2 on data handling).

Reverting to Fig. 14a, an economic arrangement for handling this retiming employs a retiming store common to several links (six or eight), with the execution of the demultiplexing for all these links under the control of a common demultiplexing control store. The arrangement of Fig. 14a in conjunction with that of Fig. 11 therefore yields a basic switch which can handle between 100 and 200 lines.

3.3.5 Connection of subscribers and the concentrator problem

So far, the outline has been confined to the tandem-switch function. Much recent work on electronic switching has tended towards the idea that a subscriber or terminal exchange is most logically built up of a tandem section working in co-operation with a number of subscribers' line concentrators. This is a particularly attractive concept in the context of p.c.m. switching.

Fig. 17 shows a functional outline of an appropriate arrangement.

In the heart of the switching centre there is a tandem switch inter-connecting p.c.m. multiplex links. Many of these links, however, are not interoffice junctions, but the input and output of 'codecs' (i.e. coders plus decoders) handling local subscribers via concentrators. These concentrators may be inside the office or remote from it. Apart from the inevitable differences in signalling and control, there

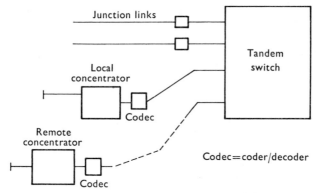

Fig. 17   Functional outline of local office as tandem switch with concentrators

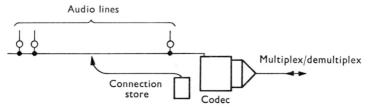

Fig. 18   Outline of p.c.m./p.a.m. concentrator

is no basic difference between the two cases, and the handling of the voice intelligence is the same in both. The validity of this process is not fundamentally dependent on the type of concentrator used, but the t.d.m. basis on which the associated p.c.m. link operates greatly increases the attractiveness of t.d.m. (p.a.m.) as the crossoffice switching mode for the concentrator.

Fig. 18 shows the outline of such a concentrator in greater detail. A p.c.m. coder associated with a multiplex link must execute its functions by taking an amplitude sample of each channel in turn.

Similarly, the decoder must deliver an amplitude sample. Normally, in the junction case, this sampling is confined to the channels (say 24) connected to a given link. If, however, the samples are related by a regular t.d.m. connection store to 24 out of, say, 200 subscriber lines, a local concentrator switch is created out of this p.c.m. time-division sampling function, which is the inescapable preliminary to a p.c.m./t.d.m. multiplex structure.

It should be borne in mind, however, that the concentrator design adopted should be determined solely on the basis of the economics of concentrator design and construction. With regard to the performance advantages of a p.c.m. switched network, the actual switching mode in the concentrator is not particularly relevant.

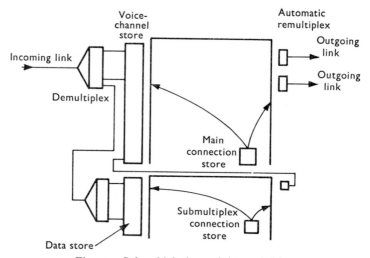

Fig. 19   Submultiplexing and data switching

3.3.6 Submultiplexing and data switching

Before concluding this brief outline of switching principles, the basis of a possible parallel switched network, or networks, for handling data will be mentioned. The whole subject of p.c.m./data integration is covered in much more detail in Section 4.2.

Fig. 19 shows, for a voice channel in a link, how the demultiplexed character, instead of being transferred to the voice memory, may be

32

passed down for a further stage of demultiplexing, to create a number of medium- or low-speed data channels or a combination of the two. The intelligence arriving in these is first transferred to a data store, and it is then transferred across the office in the same general way as for the voice intelligence, to be reassembled on the far side into its appropriate position in the outgoing multiplex. The Figure shows the reassembled character transferred to a spare incoming-voice-channel store; this arrangement gives considerable flexibility in timing.

The only major difference between the switching processes for voice and data is that the former intelligence, in most systems examined, is handled in characters, whereas data are handled in bits. These bits are reassembled into the voice-channel character at the far side of a data switch, and transferred to the outgoing link. As already pointed out, for simplicity and flexibility, this final transfer may occur, as shown, across the voice switch.

3.3.7 Key advantages of p.c.m. switching

Setting aside the transmission advantages of a switched p.c.m. network, which are dealt with elsewhere (see Section 5.1.2), the inherent advantages of p.c.m. switching may now be briefly reviewed. Three salient points can be noted:

(i) For years, t.d.m. switching has been potentially attractive for handling speech, because of its very efficient use of a limited number of 'crosspoints'. As applied to the p.a.m. mode, transmission difficulties arising from crosstalk, lack of uniformity in net overall gain etc. made its application difficult, and the need for relatively expensive line 'modems' (i.e. modulators plus demodulators), with their filter costs, have upset the economics. These difficulties, however, all disappear when the intelligence transferred is purely digital, as in p.c.m.

(ii) F.D.M. transmission involves multiplexing and demultiplexing as functions which cannot readily be combined in any way with switching, whether of time-division or space type. With p.c.m./t.d.m. line transmission and switching, these multiplexing functions are so intimately integrated with switching that it is impossible to define boundaries.

(iii) A p.c.m.-switching stage can handle signalling and control information as well as speech and data information. This means that the exchange control circuit can be directly connected to the switching stage, and so it can interchange information directly with distant switching stages (i.e. the signalling function) or with other parts of its own switching stage, such as local junctors (i.e. the control function).

3.3.8 Signalling and supervision

An integrated transmission/switching system using p.c.m. can provide a wide range of signalling and supervision techniques. First, conventional v.f. signalling can be used where necessary. Secondly, the equivalent of outband signalling may be created by adding a signalling bit to each character. This, at a slight increase in bandwidth, gives a capability for very versatile and high-speed signalling. However, the cost of monitoring and interpretation on a per-channel basis still remains; and, for this reason, much thought has been given to the use of common-channel (or order-wire) signalling.

The submultiplexing procedure already outlined (and examined in much greater detail in Section 4.2) makes available very cheaply a channel of adequate speed, and this process is highly compatible with the use of modern common electronic control of the switching function. This process is closely in line with current CCITT studies on the type-6 signalling system (CCITT, 1964*b*).

There is therefore a strong case for such an order-wire technique becoming the main basis for working in a fully integrated system; in which case, inband (v.f.) or semi-inband methods would find their place mainly in relation to such problems as interworking with traditional systems during the transitional period. This transitional period, however, is likely to last very many years.

3.4 Basic advantages and disadvantages of p.c.m.

The principal fundamentals of p.c.m. having been dealt with in Sections 3.1, 3.2 and 3.3, it is now appropriate to enumerate briefly the main differences between p.c.m. and f.d.m. (or other analogue systems). The many advantages will be seen to justify the current intense interest in p.c.m. Some of these points will be discussed further in later Sections.

Briefly, the chief differences are as follows:

(*a*) With p.c.m., overall transmission is largely unaffected by normal fluctuations in the transmission medium, provided that the transmission degradations are not allowed to exceed certain limits at any point. An adequate design margin to ensure this can be engineered quite economically. This desirable feature of a transmission system is sometimes termed 'ruggedness'.

(*b*) The ruggedness of p.c.m. *vis-à-vis* f.d.m. is a very useful attribute when several transmission systems must follow similar routes or converge on a single terminal. This ruggedness permits exceptionally good frequency occupancy for p.c.m., which offsets the basically wider bandwidth required. Allowing for the need for additional pulses for signalling and synchronisation in the case of p.c.m., and for vacant frequency bands to facilitate the filtering off or addition of channels at branching points in f.d.m. systems, the ratio of bandwidth required per channel between the two systems is of the order of 9:1.

(*c*) P.C.M. can accept high levels of line noise or crosstalk, or both. As shown in Section 3.5, a minimum signal/noise ratio (i.e. peak signal power to r.m.s. noise power) of 14 dB for binary transmission (20 dB for ternary) is satisfactory for speech. This can be compared with a typical minimum repeater-section figure for a main-line f.d.m. system of, say, 60–70 dB. Thus, p.c.m. requires much less signal power, even though the noise power is increased by virtue of the greater bandwidth of the signal.

(*d*) While the regenerative-type repeaters of p.c.m. are relatively closely spaced (typically 2000 yd for 24-channel systems on deloaded audio cables), they are also relatively cheap compared with analogue-type repeaters.

(*e*) As a very generalised cost statement, p.c.m. compares very favourably with its competitors when all aspects, including signalling, are considered. When the field of junction-area application embraces city areas, where new cable becomes excessively costly because of the expense incurred with major road disruptions, the cost picture becomes vastly more favourable to p.c.m.—under these conditions, p.c.m. can prove preferable at very short distances. F.D.M. does not really enter this cost-comparison picture, since the relatively low-grade cable facility (i.e. deloaded audio) is an unsuitable bearer for large-scale application of f.d.m.

(*f*) A transmission facility such as p.c.m. based on digital operation is much more readily suited to the handling of digital-data traffic than one based on analogue principles. The expected upsurge in data traffic foreseen in Section 5.1.5, which could become even more significant given a cheap digital-transmission capability, makes this quite an important feature.

(*g*) For the transmission media of the future, such as optical waveguides, a digital transmission method such as p.c.m. may well prove to be the only practicable system (see Section 3.2.2).

(*h*) The t.d.m. feature of p.c.m. can lead to ready combination of switching and transmission in an integrated network. The multiplexing/demultiplexing functions of f.d.m. do not readily lend themselves to combination with either space or time switching.

(*i*) In general, a p.c.m. terminal equipment providing a given number of channels will be found to contain considerably more components than a corresponding f.d.m. system. A high proportion of these, however, consist of resistors, capacitors and semiconductor devices which do not, in general, need very close tolerances, and which, moreover, are already manufactured in large quantities for the computer and data-processing fields; whereas f.d.m. systems demand close-tolerance high-grade inductors, capacitors and quartz crystals for the many filters, as well as quantities of relatively expensive wideband transformers. In practice, therefore, there is, at the present time, little difference in the overall cost per channel. As progress is made in thin-film and integrated-circuit techniques, these will be much more widely applicable to digital circuits, and the advantage in equipment costs may be expected to move steadily in favour of p.c.m.

36

3.5 Performance characteristics of p.c.m.

This Section outlines some of the more salient characteristics of p.c.m., which are as follows:

(a) The relationship between signal/noise ratio on the line and the probability of error in the received signal is one wherein the bit-error rate is rather a sharp function of signal/noise ratio. Assuming a symmetrical binary signal, the relationship of the peak-signal-power/average-'white'-noise-power ratio (in decibels) to the bit-error probability is shown in the first two columns of Table 1.

For a ternary signal such as a.m.i., and where the amount of noise is fixed, the signal/noise ratios need to be increased by 6 dB. For the practical case, where the noise is mainly crosstalk, the difference is 4·5 dB (see Section 6.2.1).

For a typical p.c.m. system with 8 kc/s sampling and 8 bits/character, the channel bit rate is 64 kbit/s, and the third column of Table 1 shows how frequently errors would occur on the average in such a system. For satisfactory speech, a bit-error probability of 10^{-6} or better is acceptable (a signal/noise ratio of, say, 14 dB), which implies about one error per minute. Practical repeaters usually need about 2 dB more margin than these theoretical figures.

Table 1 *Relationship of the peak-signal-power/average-'white'-noise-power ratio to the bit-error probability*

Signal/noise ratio (dB)	Bit-error probability	Approximate average time between errors for a bit rate of 64 kbits/s
7·3	10^{-2}	1·56 ms
11·4	10^{-4}	156 ms
13·6	10^{-6}	15·6 s
15·0	10^{-8}	26 min
16·0	10^{-10}	43·4 h
17·0	10^{-12}	180 days

(b) The process of quantisation introduces distortion which acts subjectively as noise. This quantising noise controls the message/noise ratio in p.c.m. systems. If (as is usual) the code transmitted

37

corresponds to the nearest discrete step immediately below the actual sample value, there may be an error up to a maximum of just under a complete step. This error is reduced, in practice, to a maximum of half a step, by arranging that the receiver interprets a given code as representing a voltage midway between the actual value corresponding to it at the sending end and the next step above this value.

Assuming that the message voltage is large compared with a single quantising step (or, more accurately, assuming uniform probability density over the step size), and assuming a linear transfer characteristic, the r.m.s. error introduced is $1/(2\sqrt{3})$ times the height of a single quantising step (i.e. independent of signal power). Thus, the ratio of peak-to-peak message voltage between clipping levels to the r.m.s. noise voltage equals $2b^n\sqrt{3}$, which, for binary coding, becomes $(10\cdot8 + 6n)$ decibels.

An audio tone is at least 9 dB down on the peak-to-peak excursion, and a speech signal with moderate peak clipping is 14–20 dB down. Thus, a true message/noise ratio is of the form $(6n - k)$, where k varies according to the nature of the signal and lies between the approximate limits $-2 \leqslant k \leqslant +9$. Thus for moderately good speech at constant volume ($k = +3$, say) and for a target message/noise ratio of 26 dB, n must be $\geqslant 5$ (i.e. 32 quantising levels), which agrees with practical experience.

It will be seen that the message/noise ratio improves by 6 dB for every additional binary digit, provided, of course, that the signal power is increased sufficiently to allow for the increased noise bandwidth and to maintain operation above the error threshold.

For the case of a nonlinear transfer characteristic (i.e. with companding), the quantising-distortion r.m.s. error is no longer independent of signal power. The improvement to be obtained from companding, which is greatest for the weakest signals, depends on the degree of compression. For a logarithmic compression characteristic of the form (Smith, 1957)

$$v/V = \log\left(1 + \frac{\mu e}{V}\right) \Big/ \log\left(1 + \mu\right)$$

(where v is the output voltage, e the input voltage, such that

$$0 \leqslant e \leqslant V,$$

and μ the degree of compression), the companding improvement for weak signals varies from about 24 to 30 dB for values of μ over the range $100 \leqslant \mu \leqslant 1000$. Another way of looking at this is to say that companding is equivalent to the addition of 4 or 5 digits, which would be required in the noncompanded case to obtain the same error rate.

Since quantising distortion is present only during conversation, it is the message/noise ratio which is the important parameter, rather than the absolute level of the noise which is subjectively controlling during silent intervals in conventional transmission systems. Generally, transmission quality is satisfactory for message/noise ratios greater than 20 dB.

(c) Being a quantised system, p.c.m. is also liable to peak and centre clipping. The extent of this effect depends on the volume range. When a speaker is speaking at substantially constant volume as measured by one of the types of volume indicator in common use, the instantaneous power varies over a considerable range—some 30–40 dB for significant fractions of the time. In addition, the actual volume as measured will itself vary widely with different speakers and conditions. In combination, a total volume range of some 60 dB is involved. With an analogue system, the volume range which can be handled adequately is determined on the one hand by the overload point (usually not very sharply defined), which, if exceeded, will distort the peaks of signals from the loudspeaker, and, on the other, by the noise level which will mask the lower levels (i.e. consonants) of the quiet speaker.

Both of these effects in the analogue system are rather gradual in their onset. With a quantised system such as p.c.m., however, it will be evident from Fig. 4 that any signal which exceeds the maximum (positive or negative) quantising level will be transmitted as the code corresponding to that level, however large the signal may be; so that the effects of overload or 'peak clipping' are extremely sharp. Similarly, depending on the exact location of the centre datum line AB in Fig. 4 relative to the adjacent quantising levels (in general practice, it will be somewhere between two levels), there will be a certain minimum signal voltage below which no code change can be produced, and hence such signals will not be encoded at all. This

39

effect, usually described as 'centre clipping', will first become evident with the low-level consonants of the quieter speakers.

In designing a p.c.m. system, it is important to know for what volume range the system is to be designed, the statistical distribution of signal voltages associated with that range, and the extent to which the distorting effects of the above two types of signal clipping can be tolerated. It will be evident that, for a given total number of levels and maximum acceptable voltage, the nonlinear type of quantiser, as shown in Fig. 5, which has much smaller steps in the centre of its range, will be less affected by centre-clipping distortion.

No standards have yet been generally agreed relating peak and centre clipping to the subjective performance of a system with a speech input at constant volume. However, most approaches lead to comparable results, namely that for parameters which have become conventional for junction systems (8 kc/s sampling, 128 levels and about 25 dB of approximately logarithmic companding), satisfactory speech quality is associated with a ratio (r.m.s. signal)/(r.m.s. noise) of about 23 dB.

3.6 Alternative modes of digit coding for transmission of analogue information

It has been stated on p. 12 that, in a multichannel p.c.m. system, there is a sampling device for each individual channel, followed by a quantiser/coder common to all channels. Such a quantiser performs its function on each pulse presented to it as a discrete operation not related in any way to the levels of previous pulses from the same or other channels. If it is acceptable to allocate an individual sample store to each separate channel, an important possibility immediately arises—that the quantising and coding process on any one sample can be determined by what has gone before; so that it is only necessary to indicate how the signal has changed since it was last sampled. The simplest form of such a digitising arrangement is known as delta modulation (or single-digit p.c.m.), and a more sophisticated form is known as log-differential p.c.m. Basically, the latter is equivalent to straight p.c.m. with pre-emphasis, although the result is achieved via different instrumentation.

3.6.1   Delta modulation (Deloraine et al., 1946)

In this system, one of two conditions only is transmitted to line after each sampling instant, as either a positive or negative single pulse representing a basic unit of magnitude. At any sampling instant, the sample voltage is compared with a second voltage obtained by integrating all signals which have previously been transmitted. If the sample is greater than this sum, a further 'plus' signal is transmitted, and if it is less, a 'minus' signal is sent. Speech can be reproduced at the receiving terminal by using an integrating circuit similar to that used in the sending equipment. Fig. 20 shows waveforms typical of a delta-modulation system.

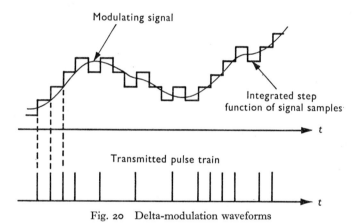

Fig. 20   Delta-modulation waveforms

The number of pulses sent to line in a given time depends on the rate of change of signal amplitude with time. Thus, a signal such as speech, in which the signals of peak amplitude (i.e. vowels) are mainly low-frequency sinusoids (with one or two low harmonics), and the high-frequency components are mainly associated with low-level signals, will require fewer digits per unit time than a signal in which the peak amplitude can be due to a high-frequency sinusoid.

Thus, delta modulation is particularly suited to the speech spectrum, but not so suited to signals having a more uniform energy/frequency distribution (e.g. multifrequency signalling, f.d.m. speech-channel groups etc.). On the other hand, the coding is inefficient, providing, as it does, only two possible output levels per sample.

The quantising-distortion power produced with such a system will clearly be a function of both the size of the quantising step used and the frequency of sampling. For a speech channel, the sampling frequency may be from 20 to about 300 kc/s, according to the grade of circuit required.

It will be evident that, with such a system, overloading will occur, owing, not to the absolute magnitude of the signal, but to the rate at which the magnitude is changing. The maximum sinusoidal signal which can be handled will therefore diminish by 6 dB/octave. Since, as already stated, speech power tends to be more concentrated in the range below about 1 kc/s, this is not a real disadvantage for speech transmission. A more uniform overload/frequency characteristic could, of course, be obtained by inserting a suitable pre-emphasis network before the quantising unit, with a complementary network at the receiving end.

3.6.2 Log-differential p.c.m. (Cutler, 1950)

This system is a logical derivative of delta modulation, and, like that, it can avoid an unnecessary number of transmitted levels for speech. At the quantising stage, the difference between the new sample and the integrated sum of all previous coded transmissions is quantised in the same manner as with normal p.c.m., but using a comparatively small number of levels having a roughly logarithmic law relating adjacent quantum sizes, as already indicated in Fig. 5. The sampling frequency for such systems will not usually be much different from that for normal p.c.m., but the number of levels required (and hence the line-frequency bandwidth required per channel) is less. While there is a need for much more subjective testing, results so far seem to show that a suitably designed system with only 16 levels (requiring ideally only four binary digits per sample) can give an overall performance approximately similar to a straight p.c.m. system using 32 levels at optimum speech volume, and using perhaps 64 levels where volume range is the limiting factor.

Like delta modulation, the log-differential method has the drawback that it is more suited to speech spectra than to any others. Thus, for example, the system is not an ideal one for multifrequency signalling, although it does appear that any resulting intermodulation terms will nevertheless be tolerable.

3.6.3 Possible applications

Owing to the increased quantity of equipment required per channel, it is probably safe to say that delta-modulation systems are unlikely to find general application in commercial telecommunication networks, but they may find uses in military or other specialised fields. Log-differential p.c.m., on the other hand, has still to be properly evaluated. In an integrated digital-transmission and switching system, for instance, although the saving in frequency band in the line system may not be of great significance, the reduction in the number of digits required to be handled by the switching equipment could conceivably prove an important economic factor. Such an integrated network of the future would also probably employ digital methods for the signalling paths, so that the log-differential p.c.m. would only have to deal with speech-type signals.

4 SUPPLEMENTARY CONSIDERATIONS

In addition to the potentialities for economic high-performance handling of speech, the use of p.c.m. on an extensive scale would open the way to the exploitation of some highly attractive and important ancillary usages. Two possibilities are outlined in this Chapter.

First, the readily applied adjunct of encryption is briefly assessed; the many technical aspects of the application of data to p.c.m. networks are then examined in some detail. Particular emphasis is given in the latter examination to the questions of system speed and sub-multiplexing (already briefly referred to in Section 3.3.6), and some typical practical applications are discussed.

The conclusions to be drawn from this data review are that much more work needs to be done before a complete assessment can be made of data integration; but it seems certain that its problems and potentialities must be carefully allowed for in planning the future of p.c.m. The problem must be considered as much more than finding ways of adapting a new type of network to the conveyance of existing classes of digital messages in a substantially traditional way. It is necessary to foresee how a new generation of terminal equipment and a new network facility can evolve on a co-operative basis with the maximum advantage to both.

4.1 Encryption

It has been widely accepted for some time that, for applications in military and diplomatic areas, the digital coding of speech is the most practicable way of providing security of communications against eavesdropping or tapping. There has been a tendency to regard this as of little consequence in commercial communications, but, more recently, several writers including Pierce (Pierce, 1964) have queried this assumption. There are probably many occasions in business

44

transactions when, in the present situation, the absence of adequate safeguards of this type is forcing long journeys and direct contact, instead of the more convenient telephone.

There is no significant technical difficulty in providing two parties on a p.c.m. digital system with quite high standards of security and guarantees of privacy. There are, however, certain system-organisation considerations which must be complied with if the facility is to succeed. The most important is that the digital-encryption methods and codes must be peculiar to the two parties or their particular 'family'. For this reason, digital coding and the return to voice must take place at the terminal instruments, which is contrary to all regular p.c.m. practice so far described. There is, however, no difficulty in separating the coding/decoding and multiplexing/demultiplexing functions; and, if this is done, the digital products of individually coded lines, and of lines sharing a common coder, may be multiplexed together in the same transmission media, and, indeed, they may share the same channels without restriction.

The attraction of such a facility for secure speech could well be limited unless it were available on long-distance connections; and such connections provide a more difficult problem economically for digital speech than do short- and medium-haul connections, owing to the more conspicuous proportion of cost attributable to sheer bandwidth. This does not, however, render the provision of such a service impracticable, and it might well be completely reasonable to provide such a long-haul facility on a scale adequate for this special requirement at a somewhat higher tariff than for other long-haul facilities. Indeed, the provision of a limited special network at somewhat increased rates might be an important element in facilitating the transition of a long-haul network into the digital method of transmission.

4.2 Handling of data

A transmission facility based on digital operation at speeds of the order of 50–60 kbit/s per voice channel opens the way to highly convenient and economic handling of large quantities of data and related

45

types of intelligence (e.g. text, black-and-white facsimile etc.). Section 5.1.5 shows quantitatively that it is possible to foresee a definite requirement in the future for quite considerable quantities of such commercial digital-intelligence transmission.

Such a marriage of analogue and digital intelligence over digital-transmission networks has already evolved in the military sphere of communications, and, while the dominant military reason for turning to a digital network has only limited relevance in commercial applications, the military operations have nevertheless shown the feasibility and economic attractiveness of the digital-network concept. Furthermore, these military networks will result in the generation of increasingly large volumes of digital intelligence; and, since effective partnership between military and commercial networks is obviously to the advantage of both, it seems highly desirable to achieve some minimal standardisation for such digital operation over commercial networks. The criterion of compatibility that should be invoked is not that of direct interworking between military and civil terminals on a digital basis, but rather that of capability of handling military intelligence with minimal special processing.

The following is an attempt to put the key issues concerning p.c.m. data integration into perspective.

4.2.1 Types of data usage

The potential demands for data transmission range from high-speed interchange between computers, at speeds of the order of 1 Mbit/s, down to text transmission at speeds comparable with current telegraph practice. This data-transmission requirement must therefore be regarded, not as data transmission over a new class of speech channel, but as the use of transmission media by t.d.m. (instead of f.d.m. as hitherto) to provide a range of digital transmission channels of varying speeds, including the speed appropriate for speech. This latter will probably be the dominant class of channel, but it should not be the only one.

Fig. 21 illustrates the ways in which, at a terminal exchange, the p.c.m.-transmission capability might be made available to a number of different types of user.

46

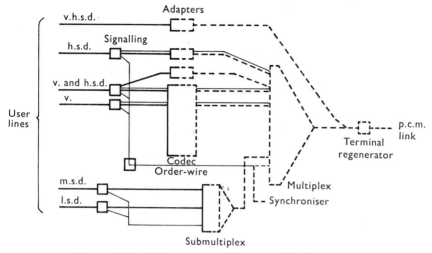

Fig. 21   Terminal arrangements for p.c.m./data integration

Continuous/broken lines indicate *approximately* the division analogue/digital p.c.m. of the intelligence signals. Thin lines relate to signalling paths

4.2.2 Basic data-system speeds

If a network providing the sort of facility shown in Fig. 21 is to materialise, considerations of simple arithmetic make it economically necessary for the bit speeds of basic channels in different classes to bear a simple integral relationship with one another. Before attempting to put figures to this concept, it is necessary to go back to p.c.m. speech developments, which are the first and motivating force in this digital field. While agreement among various authorities is anything but complete, it would appear that the p.c.m. system, which is emerging as the likely standard for application to deloaded audio pairs, and from which further expansion of the p.c.m. concept into the toll and trunk network will stem, will have the following characteristics:

(i) speech sampling at 8 kc/s

(ii) a speech character of 7 bits basic (128 levels) plus an eighth bit for signalling and supervision, and perhaps for distributed synchronisation also

(iii) a character-interleaved multiplex structure

47

(iv) a line capacity of 24 time slots, yielding 23 useful voice channels and one synchronisation channel, or 24 channels with distributed synchronisation.

Thus the line bit rate becomes $8 \times 8 \times 24$ kbit/s $= 1\cdot536$ Mbit/s.

The first data-handling capability is therefore for very high-speed data (v.h.s.d.) up to $1\cdot536$ Mbit/s. Such a service would be unlikely to be switched, at least initially, but it might find application on a private-wire basis. The next data capability indicated is that of the speech channel, which, if the same signalling capacity as is provided for voice is retained, provides a high-speed-data (h.s.d.) capability of up to a maximum rate of 56 kbit/s. Lower rates, such as 48, 40 and 32 kbit/s could, of course, also be employed.

For lower-speed capabilities, submultiplexing can be adopted, first to develop 8 kbit/s channels from the 8 bit character of the voice channel, and then, by simple counting, to yield a binarily related series of 16 channels of 4 kbit/s, 32 channels of 2 kbit/s etc. Although special users might have a demand for almost any channel in this series, it would obviously be quite impracticable and uneconomic to consider the availability of general-purpose switched networks for more than two or three of these speeds. In the derivation of these low-speed bit streams from a voice-channel bit rate, there will come a time when the transmission cost of a bit is so little that further reduction becomes uneconomic, since the gains on line cost will be outweighed by the actual t.d.m. costs. For the purpose of developing this concept a little further, it is therefore proposed that 2000 and 500 bit/s should be considered as the basic medium-speed-data (m.s.d.) and low-speed-data (l.s.d.) capabilities, respectively; although, as indicated in Section 4.2.3, even this latter facility may prove uneconomic.

4.2.3 Switching of data and the effect on user speeds

As already discussed in Section 3.3.4, the problem of switching in an integrated network is dominated by the question of synchronisation of the exchanges. Both synchronous- and quasisynchronous-network solutions were propounded. Fig. 22 shows the essentials of a tandem data switch based on quasisynchronous operation and designed to handle all four services, i.e. voice, h.s.d., m.s.d. and l.s.d. Not all of the centres in a network will necessarily incorporate data switching; at others, the bit streams could be simply patched through to constitute longer junctions between actual switching centres or longer subscriber lines, as the case may be.

In this type of quasisynchronous system, it is expected that a

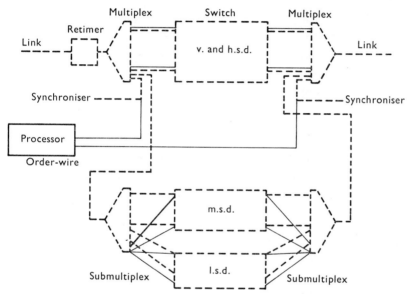

Fig. 22   General layout of a full-capability tandem switch

very large proportion of the data will be capable of tolerating the low error rate occasioned by slip (see Section 3.3.4), either by accepting it or by applying independent feedback control (e.g. block repetition). Insofar as slip will produce errors, the number due to this cause (one bit, say, in 10^6 or 10^7 omitted or repeated) is likely to be less than that due to noise and interference (one bit, say, in 10^5). However, with certain types of message signal, the results arising from the disturbance of frame synchronism, for instance, may be more damaging. In these cases where slip is intolerable, advantage may be taken of the cheap nature of the transmission to apply redundancy, preferably nominally integral (say 3:1 or 4:1); so that each user bit will correspond to several consecutive bits in the system channel. Redundancy of such magnitude, assuming a Gaussian distribution of errors, would transform an error rate of 1 in 10^5 into one of 6 in 10^{10}, which is as near perfect as most users are likely to need. Thus, additional data capabilities in the three services might be provided as follows:

(i) h.s.d.—3:1 redundancy at speeds such as 16 kbit/s

(ii) m.s.d.—4:1 redundancy at speeds such as 500 bit/s

(iii) l.s.d.—various redundancies could provide low-speed telegraphy at 125, 100, 50 bit/s etc. 75 bit/s is also feasible, but the redundancy is not integral, and the processing is therefore not so simple.

It is a possible ultimate conclusion that the bandwidth cost of the 2 kbit/s system would be so low that, except perhaps on very long-haul connections, there would be no economic justification for the creation of a 500 bit/s network. If all low-speed data were to use the 2 kbit/s network, there would be no problem at all about terminal synchronisation. With redundancies of 10:1 or more, the bit stream may be regarded as a carrier to be keyed asynchronously.

It should also be recognised that there are available established techniques for asynchronous interfaces where the user bit speed is less than the system bit rate but not by a large amount (10%, say). These use 'padding' or 'stuffing' to compensate for the speed discrepancy, and they demand only a speed margin sufficient to insert marker bits and determinate intervals to indicate the amount of 'stuffing', i.e. inserted dummy information, to be discarded at the far end.

This particular process, however, would not safeguard against mutilation by slip if the regular voice-switching capability were used. A special capability could be created, but it would be expensive, and the separation of the modes of usage would abnegate the economic gain of traffic pooling.

4.2.4 Signalling for the data systems

The current trend in p.c.m. design seems likely to make available an outband-signalling facility per voice-channel capability (1 bit/

character) and a common-order-wire capability to be used as required. Except, perhaps, for deviations in regard to number transmission (numerotation), the data connections occupying speech channels can best use the same signalling as do speech connections. On submultiplex data, the situation is more involved; the digital streams developed by submultiplexing tend to be isochronous, and interpolation of supplementary signalling information can become expensive. The cheapest way of providing an equivalent of the speech-channel extra bit is to continue the submultiplexing and derive a range of lower-speed streams, each of which may be associated with a working data channel.

The simplest way, perhaps, of achieving this is to regard each character of 8 bits as being divided into seven channels of data, and to use the eighth bit in consecutive frames as a signalling channel for each data channel in turn. To simplify the arithmetic, division by 8 rather than 7 may be recommended; this would give a basic signalling channel of 250 bit/s for 2 kbit/s data, and $62\frac{1}{2}$ bit/s for 500 bit/s data.

At the lower end of the scale, this speed is becoming low and could militate against fast signalling. It is this factor, among others, which makes order-wire or common-channel signalling attractive for a mixed network of this type. The essential issue is that, in any switched network, the provision of a high-speed-signalling capability by bandwidth redundancy is wasteful, in that it is used effectively for a small percentage only of the duration of a connection. The use of a common channel, transmitting signals when, and only when, necessary, is a considerable gain in channel efficiency, obtained admittedly at an additional processing cost.

4.2.5 Outline of a possible typical system

It is apparent that the application of data to a p.c.m.-type network is not simply a matter for a single unique transmission mode, but for a buildup of a number of modes, each appropriate to the circumstances. It is felt that this concept of an integrated voice/data network can best be clarified by outlining a typical example.

Fig. 23 shows, in very skeletal form (i.e. omitting all reference to retiming or synchronising), the essentials of a typical multiplex and submultiplex structure, wherein one of the 24 p.c.m. voice channels is employed to derive medium- and low-speed data channels as well as a synchronising character. Fig. 24 shows one possible submultiplexing pattern employing a multiframe of 16 frames, which, assuming a

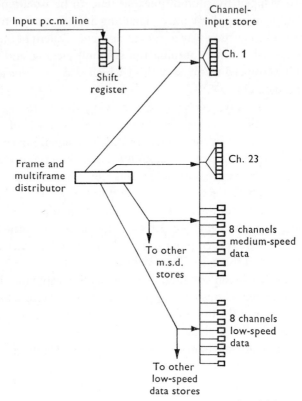

Fig. 23   Skeleton framework of typical multiplex and submultiplex structure

character-multiplexed p.c.m. system of 8 bits/character sampled at 8 kc/s, yields:

(a) 16 channels of 2 kbit/s m.s.d., of which two would be further submultiplexed to provide 16 signalling channels of 250 bit/s each

(b) 48 channels of 500 bit/s l.s.d., of which six would be further submultiplexed to provide 48 signalling channels of 62·5 bit/s each

(c) a recurrent synchronising character at 1000 characters/s.
Variants are, of course, possible on an extensive scale. For example, if, as intimated in Section 4.2.3, submultiplexing down to 500 bit/s

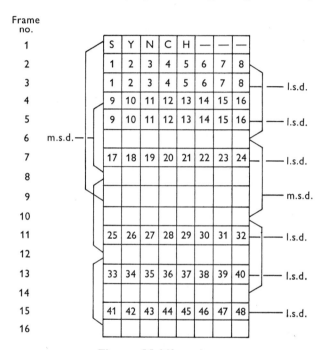

Fig. 24   Multiframe layout

cannot be economically justified, a multiframe of 32 frames would yield the same synchronising character and a total of 32 channels of 2 kbit/s m.s.d.

A typical network layout is shown in Fig. 25. This assumes that data switching is confined to the main switching centres and illustrates the use of t.d.m. channels (submultiplexed) on the 'spurs' to provide extended subscriber lines. It is also assumed that, at the data-switching centres, the switch will transfer 500 bit/s or 2 kbit/s, regardless of the mode of operation of the data terminal equipment.

53

An important element in the organisation of a satisfactory comprehensive system will be the provision of uniform, yet versatile, methods for dealing with the subscriber's line. For l.s.d., d.c. telegraph is well

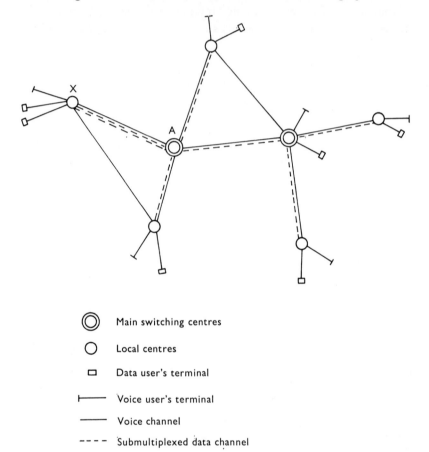

◎   Main switching centres

○   Local centres

□   Data user's terminal

├———   Voice user's terminal

———   Voice channel

- - - -   Submultiplexed data channel

Fig. 25   Typical integrated voice/data network

established, using, for certain modes, full duplex, but more generally halfduplex or switched-simplex, operation. While these modes can continue to be used for low-speed telegraph, the employment of unbalanced lines and high power levels renders them unsuitable for extension to higher speeds, as well as making it desirable to adopt more

54

appropriate low-power-transmission methods for future low-speed machines. Bearing in mind that duplex working is desirable, that there will be clocking problems for synchronous data transmission in a quasisynchronous digital network and that it is desirable to maintain 2-wire lines if possible, then, since the most convenient way of providing clocking to the terminal from the parent exchange, regardless of the presence or absence of any intelligence in the return stream, is probably the use of dipulse transmission, which always carries a clock-rate content, a rational arrangement for higher speeds could be achieved by the following:

(i) dipulse transmission to the subscriber at 500 bit/s or 2 kbit/s and forward transmission by frequency-shift keying of a carrier at approximately 20 kc/s; these should be adequately separable

(ii) up to 8 kbit/s on a similar basis to (i) if it can be managed

(iii) using 4-wire lines for 56 kbit/s, unless a narrowband (say 2 kbit/s) return channel is accepted, in which case, dipulse may be used each way, there being sufficient room for separation by filters; these principles could also, in case of difficulty, apply to 8 kbit/s, 16 kbit/s etc.

As far as processing at the terminal–user interface is concerned, the following points briefly outline considerations that may arise when accommodating the various classes of data into a quasisynchronous system:

(i) Nonredundant m.s.d. demands system clocking of the terminal, and merely a phase correction buffer at X (Fig. 25).

(ii) 4:1 redundant m.s.d. should also preferably adopt system clocking, which, as before, reduces the interface problem simply to one of phase correction; if clocking is not acceptable, a regenerator interface is required.

(iii) Nonredundant h.s.d. demands system clocking and interface conversion between bunched speech characters and isochronous data bit streams.

(iv) 4:1 redundant h.s.d. should also preferably adopt system clocking; character assembly is required at the interface. In the receiving direction, the user's isochronous delivery would

55

need to be capable of speed adjustment to line up with phase jumps resulting from slip.

(v) High-speed black-and-white facsimile should adopt something like 3:1 redundant h.s.d. (16 kbit/s) and incorporate a line-synchronising capability to permit phase recovery at the interface. Interfacing for this mode needs considerably more study.

(vi) 10:1 redundant l.s.d. (i.e. 50 baud) can accept an asynchronous interface at X.

(vii) 5:1 and 4:1 redundant l.s.d. (i.e. 100 and 125 baud) will need to employ regenerators at X, in order to maintain satisfactory distortion margins.

(viii) 75 baud telegraph could be handled asynchronously if distortion of the order of 30% maximum is acceptable; otherwise, regeneration must be employed at X, but with more expensive regenerator logic due to the nonintegral relationship of the 75 baud speed to the line-system speed.

If, as mentioned in Section 4.2.3, submultiplexing is not continued beyond 2 kbit/s, all these last three telegraph capabilities will be operating at greater than 10:1 bulk redundancy, and they can all therefore accept an asynchronous interface.

These cases obviously give only a very cursory examination of the problem, but they do, nevertheless, indicate the great potential versatility of such a system.

5 APPLICATIONS OF P.C.M.
COMMUNICATION PRINCIPLES

The previous Chapters have attempted to answer the following questions about p.c.m.:

(*a*) How did the concept arise?
(*b*) What exactly does p.c.m. do?
(*c*) How does it compare with other modulation methods?

The present Chapter will now attempt to provide an outline answer to the more important fundamental question:

(*d*) How can p.c.m. be usefully applied in communication networks?

In answering this question, consideration should be given to other possible uses, such as data and digital facsimile, as well as to the basic use for individually time-sampled and quantised telephone speech channels. The networks that will be examined under this heading are the local area, the junction area, the switched tandem network and the long-haul network. In addition, in order to assess the scope for data application, a brief traffic survey will be made of this field.

5.1 Principal network possibilities

Many possible network applications are under study; these are not independent but closely related and, to some extent, overlapping. It is possible, however, to examine them under the following five separate headings.

5.1.1 Junction carrier

This is the application already coming into commercial use on an extensive scale, particularly in the USA with the T1 carrier system (Fultz and Penick, 1965). Its use is arising as a consequence of the rapid rise in traffic over medium distances and the convenience of

57

deloaded audio cable as a transmission medium. In many urban local areas, existing cables and duct routes are already fully utilised, and the cost of providing additional similar facilities, involving, as it does, major road works in busy city areas, is so high that carrier transmission can be economically viable over about 8 miles, but this could be much less in special cases.

Much of the existing line plant of such areas, as regards noise and crosstalk, is of a standard which makes the p.c.m. mode of creating a multiplex-carrier facility more attractive than traditional methods. In addition, when all parameters, including signalling, are considered, the p.c.m. mode appears to compare favourably with its competitors on the basis of cost.

Some idea of the possible scale of application in existing audio junction cables can be obtained from studies of the crosstalk and transmission characteristics of such cables. If the p.c.m. systems are of 24-channel capacity, as is most likely (see Section 3.2.1), the capacity of the junction cables can be increased by a factor of 11 for each two pairs that can be used in the cable (i.e. allowing for the two voice circuits displaced to accommodate the p.c.m. system). Thus, if crosstalk considerations permit 60% of the cable pairs to be used, the total capacity of the cables can be increased by 7·6 times, which is quite a handsome increase.

This application to junction links (audio–audio) is, however, somewhat limited by the considerations that, in general, below a certain distance, the terminal cost makes it difficult to justify in competition with voice transmission on individual cable pairs, and, above a certain distance, its demands on bandwidth tend to create a line cost which makes competition with f.d.m. more difficult. These, however, are not clearly defined demarcations, and, over distances up to, perhaps, 50 miles, there is very little in it; the choice may well depend on the nature of the existing line plant available and on the consequences of switching integration examined in Section 5.1.2.

It has already been mentioned (Section 3.2.2) that, as the technology for handling very high bit rates becomes stabilised, p.c.m. on coaxial cable may become attractive up to considerable distances.

5.1.2 Switched tandem network

In areas where a large junction network is involved and where this includes tandem or transit switching (e.g. Paris or London), there are some obvious incentives to the introduction of p.c.m. switching and its integration with the p.c.m. junction capability. They can be itemised as follows:

(i) The use of the digital mode throughout the connection, as far as possible, takes advantage of a characteristic of p.c.m. transmission not otherwise invoked; namely, the absence of cumulative degradation (loss, distortion, noise etc.). Thus, a call involving two or more junctions would have the same overall transmission equivalent and general performance as a single-junction system, and no switching losses would be added.

(ii) With uniform transmission standards and the avoidance of switching losses, network planning and tandem switching become much more flexible. Thus, it might be convenient to make connections over a larger number of junctions in tandem than hitherto. This could lead to the use of a larger number of smaller tandem exchanges strategically located at the correct points in the area, instead of the present tendency to concentrate at one or two locations only, to avoid tandem connections involving more than two junctions.

(iii) Provided that the digital-switching economies are satisfactory, the saving in intermediate coders and decoders makes for a cheaper overall result and justifies p.c.m. over shorter distances.

(iv) Such a system provides 4-wire, rather than 2-wire, switching, with all its well known attendant advantages.

(v) As data-transmission requirements develop, the p.c.m. exchange effectively brings high-speed data facilities to the exchange end of the subscriber's loop, for exploitation as occasion offers. In future, it may be more convenient to handle telex traffic in this manner, carried as a submultiplex of the digital stream of a p.c.m. telephone channel allocated for this

59

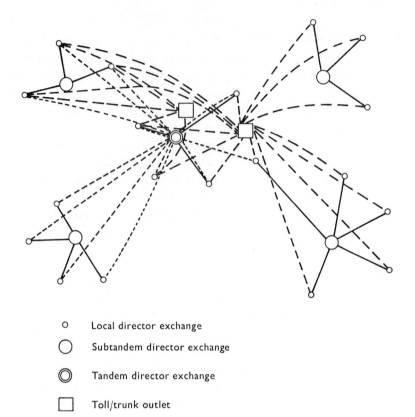

O	Local director exchange
⬭	Subtandem director exchange
◎	Tandem director exchange
☐	Toll/trunk outlet
——	Junction to subtandem
----	Junction to tandem
— —	Junction to toll/trunk outlet

Fig. 26 Simplified version of present London director step-by-step tandem network catering for subscriber trunk dialling. Only a limited number of the exchanges and routings are shown, in order not to make the Figure too confusing. All direct junctions between local exchanges have been omitted

purpose. By bringing telex right to the subscriber's exchange, it will be possible to greatly reduce the present high cost of the telex 'tails'.

(vi) Such a scheme would provide greatly improved standards of transmission loss for toll and trunk access routes. This is

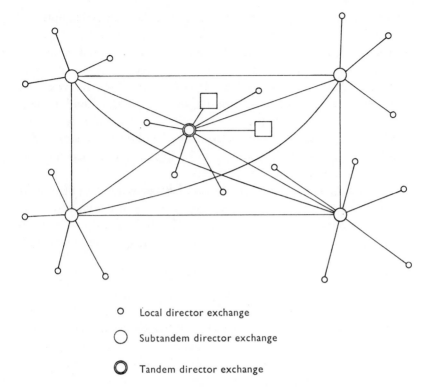

○ Local director exchange

◯ Subtandem director exchange

◉ Tandem director exchange

☐ Toll/trunk outlet

Fig. 27   How routing layout of London tandem network might be simplified with integrated p.c.m. between director exchanges. Only a limited number of the exchanges and routings are shown, in order not to make the Figure too confusing. All direct junctions between local exchanges have been omitted

important, because these tributary links are, in many cases, the major obstacle to the achievement of completely satisfactory long-haul connections.

(vii) Versatility of signalling is provided in a switched p.c.m. network.

An outline of the possible application of such an integrated scheme is shown in Figs. 26 and 27, which show a very simplified picture of the London tandem network, but which could equally well represent many other large urban areas. Fig. 26 shows the methods adopted to date based entirely on physical 2-wire circuits, with different gauges of conductor to maintain losses within the limits required for different classes of connection. Fig. 27 shows how a much simpler and more versatile layout could be achieved with switched-p.c.m. working. The contrast between these two Figures is, for the London case, much more striking than the sketches portray, since there are, in fact, nearer 200 than 20 local director exchanges, and the actual number of toll and trunk outlets is already four or five, and will soon increase with the pressure of additional traffic.

It will be noted that this application has taken no account of concentrator utilisation, which is one of the features of the limited local-area case considered in Section 5.1.3. This has been done solely to simplify the presentation and not because of any incompatibility. It is felt that a network such as that shown in Fig. 27 is viable as it stands, and concentrator usage for greater depth of p.c.m. penetration towards the subscriber would simply increase its validity.

An important economic and performance advantage of a network such as shown in Fig. 27 is the ease with which it lends itself to the introduction of separate common-channel signalling (e.g. CCITT, 1964*b*). Such signalling could make use of a data-channel facility, as described in Sections 3.3.8 and 4.2.

5.1.3 Local-area case

There is a possibility that switching p.c.m. intelligence in its digital form could be sufficiently cheap and robust to make this mode attractive for local switching. This is made more likely by the very convenient compatibility with concentrator switching. For example, a p.c.m. exchange unit might normally concentrate some 150 subscribers on to a 24-channel 'highway' to the switching equipment, and such concentrator units may, where convenient and economic, be located remote from the exchange, near the 'centre of gravity' of their subscribers. If a p.c.m. exchange were installed in the same building as a principal exchange of existing electromechanical type, it could be used to provide additional capacity in its own exchange area, as well as in conjunction with concentrators located at subsidiary exchanges in the area, providing for increasing demands in the areas of the subsidiary exchanges.

The economics of concentrator application are not wholly straightforward, particularly if the subscriber concentration is in areas served by multiconductor small-gauge cable, where the cost per pair is very low. However, it is not possible to ignore the possibility of a very different economic picture if p.c.m. characteristics and costs are used to extend very considerably the area of coverage of an exchange. In this case, concentrator economics might well take on a different complexion.

It appears, therefore, that the most promising way of introducing p.c.m. techniques into the local area on a network basis is in the provision of extensions to an existing network which is approaching saturation under the method of provision employed up to now. On the basis of normal growth figures of 6–7% per annum, such an application would soon lead to a new network superimposed on the initial network and comparable in size with it.

Fig. 28 gives in idealised form one example of how a p.c.m. exchange and its ancillary units might fit into an existing urban area. The p.c.m. exchange, because of its small size, could well fit into the existing building of exchange X. This p.c.m. exchange will perform switching operations between p.c.m. highways connecting it to the other electromechanical exchanges in the particular urban network, and to ancillary p.c.m. units (concentrators and p.a.b.x.s) if there is scope for their incorporation. Connections between the p.c.m. highways and the voice-frequency junction circuits emanating from the distant electromechanical exchanges have to be made via adaptor circuits (items A in Fig. 28) located in the old exchange building. It may also be possible to connect existing subscriber lines to the p.c.m. exchange through the adaptor.

The p.c.m. highways can be provided by pairs in the existing junction cables, the number of channels per pair (probably 24) being related to the remultiplexing arrangement in the p.c.m. exchange.

Concentrators can be used, as the Figure shows, to connect to the

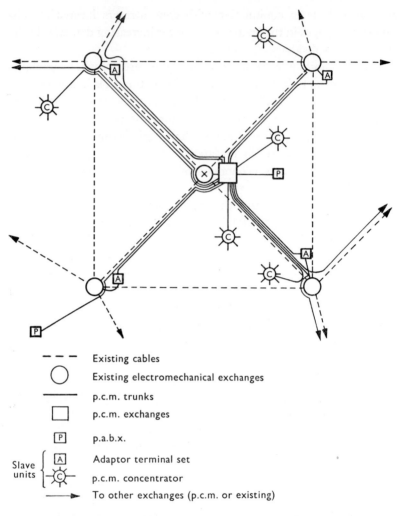

Existing cables

Existing electromechanical exchanges

p.c.m. trunks

p.c.m. exchanges

P p.a.b.x.

Slave units
A Adaptor terminal set
C p.c.m. concentrator

To other exchanges (p.c.m. or existing)

Fig. 28   Example of integration of a p.c.m. exchange (with slave units)
into an existing local area

new p.c.m. exchange subscribers who are actually in the area of the
more distant electromechanical exchanges. This arrangement permits
these new subscribers to get telephone service without disturbance to
the existing subscribers on the nearest electromechanical exchange,

and therefore without the considerable inconvenience of change of number for the existing subscribers. Here again, 24-channel capacity seems to be the most suitable size for urban applications.

As far as p.a.b.x.s are concerned, it is possible to consider them as merely connectors remotely controlled from the exchange, connecting subscribers' lines to p.c.m. highways, with interconnection between highways effected in the exchange, i.e. the Centrex concept (Weed, 1964), or else to design them as complete switching units. The choice between these solutions will be influenced by the distance between the p.a.b.x. and the exchange, and by the local traffic.

The same type of network application can be visualised if the area is rural rather than urban. Here, the subscribers tend to be located in small groups isolated from each other and at a considerable distance from the p.c.m. exchange. Both concentrators and adaptors would need to be designed for fewer channels, between 4 and 12, say, in order to find application in this environment. Where the groups of subscribers are too small to justify the setting up of a p.c.m. exchange, a satellite exchange can be used. Such an exchange would be remotely controlled by a p.c.m. exchange, with external calls transmitted in p.c.m. and local calls handled either in p.c.m. or by any other suitable switching process. In rural areas in Britain, the local traffic on small exchanges is only 10–15% of the total, and it is not unreasonable, therefore, to contemplate 'tromboning' it by p.c.m. via the distant p.c.m. exchange, which is handling all the junction traffic anyway. To 'trombone' 10% of local traffic only requires 20% extra junction capacity to the p.c.m. exchange, and this will be provided by a cheap p.c.m. facility.

5.1.4 Extension to long-haul networks

This is likely to be a slower process than the other applications considered so far, but some measure of gradual penetration might be practicable relatively soon. The main two reasons for the lack of incentive to extend p.c.m. techniques to this area are:

(*a*) The quality and economics of long-haul transmission are already considerably more satisfactory than those of the tributary networks.

(b) Since line costs for f.d.m. and p.c.m. are comparable for the same capacity, and since the proportion of the total cost attributable to the terminal equipment will be smaller for longer distances, it follows that the advantage to be obtained from p.c.m. becomes less as the distance increases.

Nevertheless, if integrated p.c.m. networks become more widely used in separate local and tributary areas, it is likely that it would become economically advantageous to consider connecting such networks together by the same p.c.m. facility. Where such connections rate as toll or medium-haul connections, application of p.c.m., at least initially, would be based mainly on the use of transmission systems with about 24 channels on symmetrical paired cables. For a major city, or for a connection between developing p.c.m. networks in, say, London and Birmingham, for example, it is more likely that requirements would be measured in hundreds of channels, and the use of small-core coaxial cable would become attractive.

While the same basic process can be used for coaxial cable (i.e. employing regeneration and enhanced noise tolerance to make available much more bandwidth than can safely be used on f.d.m. systems), the main problems in this case are more likely to be those of instrumentation than bandwidth. Instrumentation for terminals and repeaters means handling extremely high digital rates (which could reach 10–100 Mbit/s, corresponding to capacities of the order of 100–1000 channels), plus achieving flexibility (i.e. the ability to drop and insert blocks of channels at intermediate branching points on a route). The first problem of circuit techniques for handling these high bit rates has already been investigated in relation to digitised colour television (Mayo, 1964), and there seems little doubt that, before long, the required techniques will become completely practicable and commercially available. While solutions to the second problem of intermediate flexibility have not yet been developed, the basic methods seem clear enough. Thus, the two main technical problems in this field do not seem too intractable of solution.

The higher bit speed of links of this type will intensify the problems of synchronisation in relation to wander and jitter, and there has already been considerable investigation of the impact of these on the associated problems of higher-speed multiplexing and retiming.

5.1.5 Data integration

The attractions of a p.c.m. transmission network as a basis for data handling have already been outlined in Section 4.2. The difficulty arises where a national network is partly converted to p.c.m. (i.e. in the main urban areas and sporadically in less densely provided areas), while the long-haul connection remains in its present mode. This is no problem for speech, which can always return to the analogue mode. For data, however, if the economic advantages of the digital network are to be adequately realised, a suitable class of long-haul network must be created.

A view is already emerging, however, that the economic handling of data may demand the creation of a separate network, and it is certainly arguable that the viability of this would be greatly enhanced if, in many heavy-traffic areas, it could be combined with the network for p.c.m. speech, even if, over longer distances and in other areas, it had to remain, initially, at any rate, more completely independent.

However, apart from these organisational aspects, there remains the more fundamental question of whether a real need can be foreseen for digital data facilities on the scale that can readily be provided in an integrated network of this sort.

The requirements for the transfer of information with greater accuracy and at higher speed over longer and longer distances have been rapidly increasing over the past few years. The advent of electronic data-processing equipment for such purposes as accounting, inventory control, payroll processing, military processing of weapons systems data, air-traffic control etc. has led to a rapidly expanding need for communication facilities. There has also been an increasing need for the various forms of record communication, i.e. telegram, telex, facsimile, telephoto etc. Most of this information is originated in the form of digital data, and it must be delivered to a destination in the same form.

One of the most significant changes in data processing and information transfer, affecting both commercial and military fields, has been the steadily decreasing cost of computers. Faster operating times, better manufacturing techniques, programming flexibility and greatly increased storage capacity—all these factors have contributed towards making it possible for computers to do more work at less cost. At the same time, modern processing systems are oriented more and more towards real-time online operation. Because the users of a real-time system are unlikely to be located at the same place as the computer, an economical transmission plan is an extremely important element in the overall system. Moreover, because there may be a large number of different locations involved, it is often very important to keep down the cost and complexity of the equipment provided at each input/output location. Thus, although the tendency is to think of computer complexes bringing with them the need for very high speed and sophisticated communication-service requirements (and this need does, of course, exist), by far the greater preponderance of need lies in the field of relatively simple services connecting with widespread locations.

While teleprinters provide a relatively inexpensive digital input/output equipment, it is possible to look a little into the future, when the pushbutton (or so-called 'touchtone') telephone subset becomes widely established in regular telephone service. Quite apart from the fact that such an instrument will permit more rapid establishment of call connections, once the connection is set up, the instrument can be used as an effective end-to-end signalling device. Every telephone so equipped will be capable of transmitting digital information to update or to interrogate a computer.

Looking somewhat further into the future, it is possible to visualise the size and cost of computers being reduced to such an extent that personal portable computers become a possibility (Bagrit, 1964). In conjunction with this development, there would be a national computer 'grid', into which such computers could be 'plugged'. Schemes have already been devised in the USA [for example, project MAC—machine-aided cognition (Corbató et al., 1962 and Fono, 1965)], which permit 100% utilisation of the operating time of the central computer and, at the same time, permit an interrogator with a very small problem requiring minimum computer time to obtain immediate attention. Other possibilities of widespread data transmission include control of domestic cooling and heating systems from a centralised computer fed with meteorological data, and medical diagnosis via reference of symptoms back to a centralised computer (Bagrit, 1964).

Looking towards the end of the present century, it is possible to foresee (Reeves, 1965) a need for widespread closed-loop television, both for information retrieval from centralised information processing centres and for contact with one's place of employment, in order to avoid what will by then be intolerable commuting problems. Such new services will require large increases in network bandwidth, and they will probably entail the use of the optical region of the frequency spectrum. Transmission by optical means for a given signal/noise ratio is many times more efficient when digital methods are employed than when analogue methods are used.

Therefore there would seem to be every indication of large increases in digital traffic, and, although military and other government services have taken the lead in establishing digital communication systems, a similar growth in the commercial world may well generate even greater volumes of communication traffic. However, it would be as well if some actual traffic-volume figures could be produced to support these purely theoretical statements.

Taking the case of Britain, the following figures are applicable:

(a) *Telephone traffic*

The total number of originated effective inland telephone calls for the year ended the 31st March, 1965, as published by the BPO (British Post Office, 1965) was $6 \cdot 334 \times 10^9$. With an average call duration of $1 \cdot 5$ min and a total of 300 average telephone days in one year, the total traffic volume becomes $5 \cdot 28 \times 10^5$ h of traffic per day. The growth rate averaged over the six years 1959–65, during which tariff changes have not been sufficient to significantly affect growth, shows an increase in calls of $7 \cdot 8\%$ per annum. Thus, in ten years, the traffic volume would become $11 \cdot 21 \times 10^5$ h of traffic per day.

(b) *Telex traffic*

(i) *Dialled calls.* The total number of 2d. units metered for inland traffic for the year ended the 31st March 1965, as published by the BPO was $161 \cdot 114 \times 10^6$. Assuming 50 miles for an average call (i.e. a 2d. unit buys $0 \cdot 5$ min) and a total of 270 average telex days in one year, this yields a total traffic volume of $4 \cdot 97 \times 10^3$ h of traffic per day. The growth rate averaged over the three years 1962–65 (the service has only been available for 6 years) shows an increase of $27 \cdot 9\%$ per annum. Thus, in 10 years, the traffic volume would become $5 \cdot 83 \times 10^4$ h of traffic per day.

(ii) *Operator-assisted calls.* The total number of inland calls for the same period as published by the BPO was 121×10^3. Taking $1 \cdot 5$ min for the average call, and the same figure as before for the total number of working days, this yields a total traffic volume of $11 \cdot 2$ h of traffic per day.

It can be expected that the growth rate for this facility will tail off with the spread of the automatic service; so that, in 10 years, the traffic volume might only have increased to a total of say 20 h of traffic per day.

(c) *Telegraph traffic*

The total number of inland telegrams for the year ended the 31st March 1965, as published by the BPO, was only $10 \cdot 466 \times 10^6$. Since telegraph traffic is declining (averaged over the six years 1959–65, the decrease amounts to an average of $5 \cdot 65\%$ per annum), it will not be considered further in this traffic assessment.

(d) *Data traffic*

Existing data traffic, as assessed from the number of Datel-100 and -600 customers, is relatively insignificant, although the growth rate is high (136 customers at December 1965, using 376 terminals at the slower speed and 483 at the higher speed, with a 70% per annum growth rate over the two years 1964–65). For projecting future traffic, it is not unreasonable to look at the growth in computer installations, which, at June 1965, stood at 1083. While the present growth rate is averaging about 50% per annum, this is likely to tail off somewhat, to give an average of say 35% per annum over the next 10 years.

From an analysis of the varying functions for which computing centres have been set up (e.g. payroll accounting, seat reservations, production control etc.), it seems also not unreasonable that half of them would probably be potential customers for data transmission, provided that reasonably priced input/output devices were available for the remote locations.

Just how much traffic such potential customers might generate can be assessed from the peak daily figure of 2×10^6 characters quoted* by one large organisation for the total incoming and outgoing traffic, both electrical and otherwise (e.g. postal mail). Traffic figures from two large airlines for operations at their London computing centres yielded even higher quantities (for electrical data only) of 10^7 and 5×10^8 characters/day. Taking the lowest of these three figures, and assuming 8 bit/character and a 600 bit/s transmission speed, yields a potential traffic volume of 4×10^3 h of traffic per day. After 10 years, a 35% per annum growth in computers, plus, say, a 15% per annum growth in traffic, coupled with higher transmission speeds (say 1200 bit/s) yields a potential traffic volume of some $11 \cdot 5 \times 10^4$ h of traffic per day.

On this basis of traffic time per day, therefore, while the present ratio of voice traffic to digital traffic is 110:1, the potential data traffic could decrease this ratio to about 60:1; while, in 10 years' time, when the potential should have been realised, the ratio would be significantly reduced to 6·5:1.

While comparing these quantities on other bases (e.g. erlangs, number of bits etc.) is probably equally valid, the final conclusions are not likely to be significantly different. These conclusions are that, even without the appearance of such future facilities as direct computer–computer transmission, widespread digital television, and similar proposals visualised above, there is going to be a rapidly growing demand for digital communication.

* *Computer J.*, 1963, **6**, p. 230

6 BASIC SYSTEM ELEMENTS AND FACTORS AFFECTING P.C.M.-SYSTEM DESIGN

Whereas the previous Chapters have dealt only broadly with the functions performed by the basic system elements, this Chapter will aim at giving a more detailed description of some typical modes of operation of these elements (in the terminal equipment, in the regenerative repeaters, and in the switching equipment). Particular attention will be given to those factors that need to be allowed for when integrated transmission/switching networks are considered. The emphasis throughout will be on concept rather than on detailed instrumentation. Since this Chapter is more in the nature of a technical appendix, it can probably be omitted by those who only need the broad picture of p.c.m. potentialities, which has already been covered in the preceding Chapters.

6.1 Terminal equipment

The operations required in any p.c.m. terminal, shown in simplified schematic form in Fig. 29, are as follows:

(a) sampling (and the reverse process—reconstruction)
(b) time-division multiplexing (and demultiplexing)
(c) compression (and expansion)
(d) quantising and encoding (and decoding)
(e) timing to control processes (a) to (d)
(f) transmit and receive amplification

Operation (a) is required on a per-channel basis, while (c) to (f) involve equipment common to all channels. Operation (f) is achieved by regenerators, which are dealt with in Section 6.2.

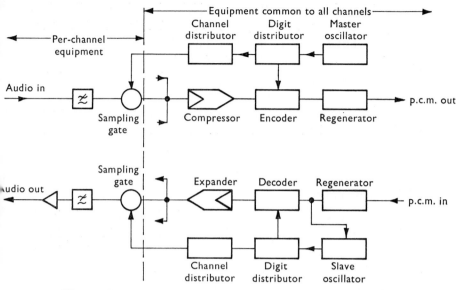

Fig. 29   Pulse-code modulation terminal—simplified block schematic

6.1.1   Sampling and reconstruction

The basic principles have been outlined in Sections 3.1.1 and 3.1.2. In practice, of course, instantaneous sampling cannot be achieved, and the p.a.m. sample pulses will have a finite duration and nonflat tops. It can be shown that the frequency spectrum will be the same as shown in Fig. 3, but with the addition of an envelope (i.e. an amplitude falloff with increasing harmonic frequency) introduced by the finite pulsewidth. In practice, the sample duration is so short (typically 4 μs) that the assumption of instantaneous sampling effectively holds good.

Similarly, the ideal low-pass filters assumed for delivering a band-limited signal to the transmitting sampling gate, and for deriving the original modulation from the receiving sampling gate, cannot be achieved in practice. Furthermore, elaborate filters which even approach the ideal would seriously impair the economic advantage to be derived from p.c.m. Even though nonideal filter characteristics must perforce produce additional noise (termed 'lower-sideband noise',

73

since it is produced from the lower sideband of the sampling frequency), it can be shown that, if the permissible increase in system noise caused by the lower sideband is limited to o·5 dB for all but the o·1% loudest speakers (which criterion gives negligible increased noise for average speakers), readily realisable filter characteristics result. If, for reasons of economy, *RC* active filters are employed, it has to be remembered that these increase the power consumption and the liability to variations in overall net gain, both of which are serious practical problems.

6.1.2 Companding

From surveys (Purton, 1962) made of telephone speech-signal statistics, concerning both the likely range of volumes in a telephone circuit and the variation in instantaneous amplitude of an individual speaker, it appears necessary for the p.c.m. system to have a range of some 60 dB between the smallest quantisation step and the peak limiting levels. This will give good-quality speech for 98% of telephone conversations, covering a volume range of ± 13 dB relative to a median speaker. To achieve uniform quality over this volume range, and achieve tolerable quality for small signals with only 128 quantising steps, an approximately logarithmic arrangement of levels is necessary. To improve still further the signal/quantising-noise ratio for small signals (with a tolerable reduction in signal/noise ratio for larger signals) without the disadvantages of increasing the degree of compression, there are advantages in adopting a compression characteristic which gives constant gain to small signals changing to a logarithmic law above a particular signal level. In practice, the logarithmic part of the compression curve is approximated with a number of linear segments (typically four or five, each covering 10–8 dB, say, of the input volume range). Even with this approximation, it is possible to achieve a signal-power/error-power ratio of 30 dB over a 30 dB volume range, with a peak clipping level of about + 6 dBm0 and a centre clipping level of about − 55 dBm0.

Logarithmic quantising may be achieved either directly from a nonlinear encoder or else from a linear encoder preceded by an in-

74

stantaneous compressor. The latter solution has the advantage of considerably reducing the range of levels applied to the input store preceding the encoder, which eases the store design from the point of view of crosstalk. However, recent designs appear to indicate a satisfactory solution to the problem of the capacitor store prior to a nonlinear encoder.

The approximation of the nonlinear characteristic by a series of linear segments permits the use of precision linear elements (high-stability resistors), which are usually switched into circuit by current switching of biased diodes. These techniques make possible the attainment of an accuracy of matching such that the compressor–expander combination yields harmonic margins better than 40 dB for quite wide temperature differences between compressor and expander.

6.1.3 Encoding and decoding

Basically, three classes of coders can be distinguished, as follows:
  (i) level-at-a-time coders, which operate by counting how many times the smallest unit is contained in the instantaneous value of the signal; if m levels are to be resolved, and the time required for each decision operation is t, the maximum coding time is mt
 (ii) digit-at-a-time coders, which operate by measuring the signal against a binary pattern of values (i.e. 1, 2, 4, 8 units etc.); the coding time in this case is $\log_2 m \times t$ where m and t are as in (i)
(iii) word-at-a-time coders, which operate by measuring the signal in one operation against the complete range of possible amplitude steps, which are all stored internally in the coder; the coding time in this case is simply t.

Operating speeds intermediate to the limiting figures quoted for these three types can be achieved by slight modification to the basic techniques. For example, in the case of the level-at-a-time coders, a preliminary coarse count with a 2-unit step followed by a fine count with the basic single-unit step, to improve the accuracy of the coarse measurement, can halve the maximum coding time. Similarly, for the digit-at-a-time coders, instead of determining, at each measurement, which of two amplitude ranges includes the signal amplitude, it is possible to determine which of four amplitude ranges includes the signal amplitude (i.e. the device becomes a two-digit-at-a-time coder), and thereby halve the coding time. Likewise, all the other steps between single-digit-at-a-time and word-at-a-time coders are possible, with the number of components involved in the design varying approximately in inverse proportion to the number of computing operations.

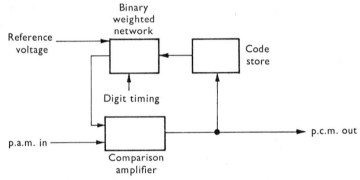

Fig. 30   Simplified block schematic of network encoder

It is apparent that there are many possible methods of achieving encoding and decoding, and it is only possible to mention one or two actual applications here. Two approaches for junction-system application (Mann *et al.*, 1962 and Chatelon, 1963) have adopted the sequential-comparison-network type of encoder and decoder. A simplified schematic of the network encoder is shown in Fig. 30. This coder successively compares the p.a.m. input with binary weighted currents generated by what is, in effect, a decoder. Thus, in the first comparison, if a 7-digit code is being generated, a timing pulse causes the binary network to subtract 64 units from the p.a.m. signal. If the residue is positive, the comparison amplifier delivers a 1 at its output, and the binary network then subtracts $64+32$ units for the second comparison. If the residue had been negative, the comparator would have delivered a 0 to its output, and the binary network would then

76

have subtracted only 32 units from the p.a.m. signal for the second comparison. This process continues until the final comparison is made for the least-significant code digit, at which time, the voltage available from the binary weighting network is equal to the p.a.m. signal to within one quantum step. For the decoding process, shown in simplified block form in Fig. 31, a reference voltage is applied to the relevant binary weighting resistor in response to each pulse in a given time slot on the p.c.m. line. Thus, the p.a.m. output will be the summation of currents proportional to the weight of the respective pulses. Since all the weighted currents must be present at the moment of demultiplexing, the decoder must contain serial–parallel

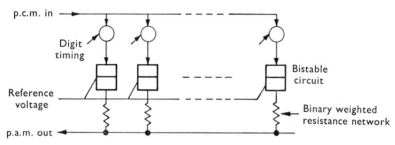

Fig. 31   Simplified block schematic of network decoder

conversion; this is provided in the decoder shown in Fig. 31 by the bistable circuits.

Another approach (Jessop and Cattermole, 1964) has also adopted the sequential-network coder; but, for the reasons outlined in Section 6.2.1, transmission problems have been eased by the restriction of the binary-coded signals to those displaying unit disparity only. Such a code, as well as requiring more digits for the same number of quantising levels (actually the redundancy is equivalent to about 1 bit), cannot be constructed with constant nonnegative weights in the binary weighting network. In fact, a constant-disparity code, in which n digits out of N are marks, requires up to n-valued weights (i.e. the weight for any particular digit varies depending on the response to the prior digits).

Yet another approach (Cattermole *et al.*, 1963) employed parallel

77

coding via a coding matrix giving a 7-digit unit-disparity unit-distance code.

For high-speed applications, an example is provided by the Bell System beam-coding tube (Cooper *et al.*, 1964) operating as a word-at-a-time coder at a frequency of 12 Mc/s for coding colour television or similar broadband signals (e.g. a 1200-channel f.d.m. 'bundle').

For relatively low-speed applications, level-at-a-time (or pulse-count) coding has been employed at a maximum rate of 3 Mc/s to provide a 6-channel 6 bit military system (sampling rate 6·67 kc/s) (Clemett *et al.*, 1964).

It will be apparent from this very brief survey of encoding/decoding that there is a considerable variety of methods available to the system designer.

6.1.4 Terminal timing control

Under this heading comes all the equipment that is necessary for the correct programming of the terminal operations covered by Sections 6.1.1–6.1.3, together with the methods for achieving synchronism and framing of receiving and transmitting terminals. The control circuits for the terminal operations are quite straightforward, consisting primarily of a crystal-controlled master oscillator running at the basic pulse-repetition rate as the source of precise timing signals. From this is derived the digit counter, supplying one pulse every nth slot (where n is the number of slots per channel) as digit-timing information to the encoder and signalling gates. From the digit counter is derived the channel counter, supplying 24 pulses for operation of the 24-channel sampling gates.

In order to maintain the transmitter and receiver of a point-to-point p.c.m. system in synchronism, two basic requirements have to be met. First, the two ends of the system must be locked in both frequency and phase, which, basically, can be achieved at the receiver by extracting the digit frequency from the incoming signal and locking a local master oscillator by means of a phase comparator. Secondly, the receiver must be able to relate the right pulses to the right channel; and therefore every frame (i.e. the aggregate speech

78

samples and signalling bits resulting from sampling each channel once) must include some distinctive signal marking the commencement (or termination) of each complete cycle of coded information.

The synchronising action can be either forward- or backward-acting. In the former case, a definite signal is sent prior to sampling the first channel, so that the system is brought into synchronism at every frame. This requires a fairly long and complicated pulse pattern, which is wasteful of bandwidth and also entails excessive frequency of framing loss on isolated transmission errors. For the preferred backward-acting case, the receiving terminal monitors the incoming signal to determine whether the system is in synchronism, and initiates a search procedure when lack of synchronism is detected. This can be arranged to ignore isolated transmission errors by insisting on a given number of errors in a specified time before deciding that the system is out of frame. Four methods are possible for the point-to-point p.c.m.-system case:

(i) The use of a modification to the transmitted pulse train (e.g. a double-width pulse or, in the case of a.m.i. transmission (see Section 6.2.1), a violation of the alternate-polarity rule—this method, while giving a quick and cheap means of establishing synchronism with a very small loss of useful-information capacity, has the basic drawback that a signal of a different type is sent, which makes different demands on the regenerator; it is also either unsuitable for cable transmission or else it restricts the system to one particular type of transmission.

(ii) The use of one extra digit per frame, as adopted in the Bell T1 system (Davis, 1962)—this method, while wasting very little information capacity, does lead to rather long acquisition times in the search procedure and, perhaps more important, to irregular frame timing, which is an impediment to multiplexing, submultiplexing and switching.

(iii) The use of single- or double-channelled time slots in each frame, for a pattern of digits which is either unique or else unlikely to be simulated by the remaining code digits—in one application (Jessop and Cattermole, 1964) of this method, where a single channel is allotted to synchronising, two specific comple-

79

mentary 9-digit u.d. characters out of the 252 characters possible are employed in alternate frames to identify the signalling channels; but, as far as the synchronising action is concerned, the two characters are equivalent. The method is relatively simple, cheap and fast; and, in the practical embodiment referred to, loss of synchronism is detected, and synchronism is regained, in under 1·8 ms [compared with up to 50 ms for method (ii)]—a time which actual operating experience has shown to be short enough to inhibit signalling errors.

(iv) The use of one extra digit in each channel time slot in a distinctive pattern—this requires about three times as many digits per frame as for method (iii), but it does not, of course, reduce the number of speech channels that are possible. Where one extra digit is employed for signalling purposes in each channel, the two functions of signalling and synchronising can be combined in this digit; but this would, of course, double the time required to recognise and achieve synchronism. The resynchronising time need not be too long for one 24-channel group, but it certainly would be for larger groups or for multiplexed supergroups.

In practice, method (iv) seems the most likely to be adopted by the CCITT as the recommended standard.

When integrated mesh-type networks are considered, the problem of synchronising becomes much more complicated, since the time scale for locally generated signals at a particular switching centre must inevitably be different from the variable time scale incurred by signals transmitted over an inherently variable medium from a distant switching centre, even if the local time scale at that distant centre was accurately synchronised with that at the first centre. This whole subject has already been covered in some detail in Section 3.3.4.

One aspect of the synchronisation problems of integrated networks that is presently the subject of considerable study is that of rapidity of recovery of synchronism. Whereas, in straight voice usage, recovery in less than 10 ms, say, is, perhaps, not very important if loss of synchronism is, itself, a fairly rare phenomenon, in a combined voice/data system, rapid recovery of synchronism could be an important contribution towards the attainment of very low error rates for medium- and low-speed data. Such rapid recovery would, of course, be of little value if loss of synchronism were always associated with a finite extended period (say several milliseconds) of lost or mutilated intelligence. However, assuming that this is not the case, and that rapid recovery is a desirable feature, with quasisynchronous operation an occasional transmission break or finite period of mutilation would cause the loss of the slave clock controlling the transfer of the incoming bit stream to the retiming store. Under this condition, operations would be so disorganised that recovery of synchronism on resumption of regular transmission would almost inescapably become a matter of resuming the full search procedure. This suggests the use of a slave clock with a very long flywheel action, when there would be a better chance of recovery based on a short search procedure, because the resumption of transmission would be nearly in synchronism anyway. One way that this might be achieved would be to modify the local clock rather than generate an independent slave clock. This would involve the following basic requirements:

(a) With a normal signal being received, the time constant of adaption to rate fluctuations (called 'stiffness') would have to be no longer, and preferably slightly shorter, than that of a regenerator.

(b) With an abnormal signal, or during the absence of a signal, adjustment of the local clock would have to cease, and the operations would have to continue on the local clock unmodified.

Such an arrangement would not appear to present insoluble problems.

6.2 Line equipment

6.2.1 Type of line signal

Most p.c.m. systems to date have been concerned with the transmission of the baseband signal rather than with any carrier techniques. However, the latter might well be considered for future longer-haul applications to coaxial cables.

The manner in which a baseband pulse train is formed for transmission is determined by the characteristics of the transmission medium. If, for example, transmission or restoration of d.c. is difficult, it would be preferable to produce a signal with no d.c. component. If h.f. crosstalk is a problem, it would be desirable to employ a scheme without excessive energy or discrete frequency components in the h.f. part of the spectrum of the signal. In the former case, i.e. where the exigencies of line transmission call for the generation of some form of signal that will not suffer unduly from the inability of the line transformers to pass d.c. or very low-frequency components, there are several possible solutions, as shown in Fig. 32. This Figure shows the various possible arrangements for handling an arbitrary 7-digit binary signal (6 bit speech plus 1 bit signalling). In order of increasing time period, over which the average d.c. level is approximately zeroed, these solutions are:

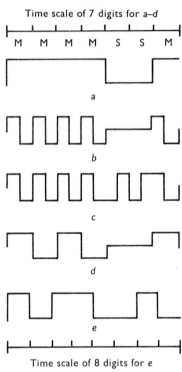

Time scale of 7 digits for a–d

M   M   M   M   S   S   M

a

b

c

d

e

Time scale of 8 digits for e

Fig. 32   Alternative forms of coded signal

a   Arbitrary binary code
b   Dipole pulses, amplitude modulation
c   Dipole pulses, phase modulation
d   Alternate-mark inversion
e   Unit-disparity code

(1) The use of dipole pulses (also known as 'dipole' transmission), which can either be a.m. (Fig. 32b) or p.m. (Fig. 32c)—this method preserves 2-level signalling, since the negative segments can be ignored at the receiver, and it also has the greatest tolerance to low-frequency cutoff of the methods proposed; but it does require a widening of the bandwidth at the high-frequency end.

(2) The use of bipolar transmission [also known as alternating

82

binary and as alternate-mark-inversion (a.m.i.)], as in Fig. 32*d*
—this is a type of pseudoternary code, in that distinguishing
of three levels is required, and the method is therefore obviously less resistant to crosstalk and noise than a method involving binary decisions only. A more refined variant (Bell
Telephone Laboratories, 1964) is now coming into favour in
the Bell system, giving greater uniformity of timing content.
This is termed pair-selected ternary (p.s.t.), and it is a redundant code derived from nonredundant binary by taking pairs of
binary digits and translating them into pairs of ternary digits
according to Table 2. For successive pairs of type 10 or 01,
code sets 1 and 2 are used alternately. At the receiver, the
incoming ternary code can be resolved into pairs by using
the fact that pairs such as 00 do not occur in the ternary-
code pairs. Another variant favoured by the BPO uses bipolar
transmission, but with only alternate digits complemented, to
improve average timing content.

Table 2   *Translation from binary digits to pairs of ternary digits*

Binary pair	Ternary pairs			
	Set 1		Set 2	
11	+1	−1	+1	−1
10	+1	0	−1	0
01	0	+1	0	−1
00	−1	+1	−1	+1

(3) The use of low-disparity code, in particular a unit-disparity
(u.d.) code such as that depicted in Fig. 32*e* (in order to maintain
the number of levels given by the 6bit straight binary speech
signal, 7 bits are required in unit-disparity code, and it is to
this 7bit u.d. code that the title of Fig. 32*e* refers. The 8-
digit signal shown includes an arbitrary signalling bit, so that
the final character actually has a disparity of 0 or ±2).

One possible variant (Carter, 1965) of low disparity is a redundant code in which complementary characters are equivalent.

It is derived from a nonredundant code by sending each character in such a sense as to reduce the accumulated disparity of the signal. One redundant digit indicates the sense chosen; and, in the case of the 8 bit 24-channel system, it involves an increase in line frequency from 1·536 to 1·728 Mc/s.

Technically, for paired-cable operations, the u.d. binary is felt to be the best solution when comparing 24-channel regenerative repeaters designed for u.d. binary with 24-channel bipolar repeaters; the following advantages are seen to accrue:

(a) As already mentioned, bipolar transmission needs a better signal/noise ratio than binary transmission. Both theory and experiment confirm that the difference is of the order of 4·5 dB. Thus, the crosstalk margin required (measured at half the bit rate) is ideally 7 dB for a.m.i. and 2·5 dB for u.d. binary; in practice, 2 dB better than this is required for both systems.

(b) For similar facilities (i.e. catering for around 128-level speech plus signalling), u.d. binary requires nine digits and a.m.i. or p.s.t. eight digits. The extra bandwidth required for the former raises the level of random noise by 0·5 dB, far-end crosstalk by 1 dB, and near-end crosstalk by 2 dB.

(c) Combining (a) and (b) and allowing for the fact that the predominant danger of digital errors arises from near-end crosstalk implies a net advantage of about 2·5 dB for u.d. binary over a.m.i. or p.s.t., which, for a given paired cable, could correspond to at least 40% more traffic.

(d) The net difference in timing jitter is negligible, being less than the scatter in observations.

(e) The binary repeater is more tolerant of signal-level fluctuations.

(f) The binary repeater consumes less power than the a.m.i. repeater.

(g) Owing to the more complex encoding and decoding process, the u.d. binary terminal costs a little more than the a.m.i. or p.s.t. type of terminal. However, because of factors (a)–(f), the binary repeaters are simpler and cheaper than those for a.m.i. Considering total system costs, with present components and techniques, the break-even point appears to occur with systems having about 11 repeaters. However, the crossover point of the cost/length lines of both systems almost coincides with the much steeper line for audio-cable costs; so that no significant difference of 'prove-in distance' is to be expected. It is, however, on the longer routes that multiplex transmission is likely to be preferred to physical cables, and here u.d. binary has the edge on a.m.i. or p.s.t.

However, despite the technical superiority of u.d. binary, little support has been received for it at international CCITT meetings, where the majority vote has been for simple bipolar (i.e. a.m.i.) transmission.

Where higher-capacity systems on longer-haul routes operating over coaxial cables are concerned, it is too early to be dogmatic on the most desirable form for the line signal. Present feelings are, however, that some form of multilevel p.c.m. or differential p.c.m.-baseband signal will eventually prove to be the best choice.

6.2.2 Regenerative repeaters

The operations that must be performed in a regenerative repeater, in order to satisfactorily reconstitute a signal that has been distorted during transmission through a bandwidth-limited medium, are those of reshaping, retiming and regenerating.

Reshaping

Reshaping involves the provision of equalisation at the input to the repeater; so that the combined overall frequency characteristic of the transmission medium plus the equaliser is such as to produce, at the input to the regenerator, a pulse train, to which it is possible to allocate a slicing level for the purpose of making a decision as to whether a mark or space is present. It can be shown that a gradual rolloff, rather than a sharp cutoff, amplitude characteristic is desirable for reducing interdigit interference. Such interdigit interference also arises from pulse echoes produced by ripples in the overall amplitude or phase frequency characteristic or both. In practice, for a pulse train employing 100%-duty-cycle pulses, a typical equalised characteristic is one that is reasonably flat up to half the bit rate, and 9 dB down, say, at the bit rate.

Retiming

A timing component, phase-locked to the received pulse train, is necessary if the regenerator is to make independent decisions on the received train on a pulse-by-pulse basis. This timing component may be either extracted from a component that naturally exists in the pulse train, added to the pulse train at the transmitting end and removed at the receiving end (e.g. a timing-wave component could be added in the spectral nulls exhibited at the bit frequency with a.m.i. transmission), or transmitted over a separate facility. In practice, designers have all adopted the first of these methods.

With a straight unipolar pulse train, there is a discrete frequency component at the bit frequency, and this component may be extracted with a resonant circuit and used to control the regenerator. The extracted component must be amplified in a high-Q factor circuit, or else the timing component will decay during long periods of spaces; elimination of the all-zero code will provide at least one mark per character to keep the timing circuits operative. The Q factor, and inversely the bandwidth of the filter, is a matter of compromise. To obtain a reasonably pure unmodulated sinewave from an input signal with virtually random modulation, a very narrow passband (i.e. high Q factor) is required. On the other hand, the phase shift of the timing wave (which should be limited to a few degrees) arising from slight mistuning of the resonant circuit is proportional to the product of Q and the frequency change; so that frequency tolerances of components set a limit to the Q factor. A Q factor of about 1000 is reasonable at most frequencies of interest.

With u.d. binary and a.m.i. or p.s.t. types of pulse transmission, the spectrum falls to zero at the bit rate, but there is a significant continuous component at half the bit rate. The timing waveform may therefore be derived by rectifying the band-limited signal and applying the train of pulses produced by the cusps of the rectified waveform (i.e. by the signal transitions) to a narrowband filter centred on the bit frequency. The effect of low-frequency cutoff is to shift the transitions in both directions, but with a predominant phase advance. With practical pattern variation, the transition displacements are irregular. However, owing to the smoothing imparted by the timing filter, the final timing wave exhibits less pattern-induced jitter. Since the more-rapid variations are more effectively smoothed, the jitter amplitude falls more rapidly with restriction of sequence length. This is where u.d. binary or p.s.t. scores over a.m.i., since the density of timing information is relatively more constant, both with time in any one signal, and between signals which may crosstalk together.

Once a timing component is available, it may be used to retime the pulse train, either partially or completely. In partial retiming, the peak of the timing wave is clamped to a reference and added to the incoming pulse train. When the algebraic sum of the timing wave plus the signal exceeds the slicing level, the regenerator becomes operative. With this method, the timing waveform can be derived from either the input signal (sometimes called forward-acting re-timing) or the output signal (sometimes called backward-acting re-timing). The former is much to be preferred, since it allows a wider tolerance on the mean frequency of the resonant extraction circuit (i.e. the noise penalty arising from increasing tuning error increases relatively slowly with the former method and quite rapidly with the latter), and, in fact, backward timing is not used at all nowadays. The retiming is partial in that noise and timing errors on the input pulse affect the timing of the leading edge of the regenerated pulse. This effect is, however, reduced as the clock amplitude increases.

With complete retiming, narrow pulses extracted from the timing waveform are used to sample the received pulse train, and a completely new output pulse is initiated if the received train exceeds the slicing level at the decision instant. The retiming is complete in that the leading edge of the regenerated pulse is completely controlled by the timing wave and largely unaffected by noise or timing errors associated with the input pulse. It is not perfect, however, since the extracted clock is still subject to jitter. Complete retiming is not difficult to instrument, and it has considerable operational advantages.

Regenerating

Amplitude regeneration, in the ideal case (also called complete regeneration), produces no output when the input is below a reference level (generally half the received peak pulse amplitude) and full output if the reference level is exceeded, even by the smallest amount. Such a step-type characteristic can be approached quite closely by means of a trigger circuit. In order to accurately control the width of the regenerated pulse, it is necessary to employ a complete retiming process (see p. 87) and to switch the trigger circuit off by a negative timing pulse rather than rely on regenerative switchoff.

For regeneration at intermediate frequencies rather than at baseband, achievement of the idealised step characteristic may not be readily realised. In this instance, resort can be made to partial regeneration where the output and the input are related, for example by a square law. In the absence of any systematic deviation, a succession of such square-law regenerators can rapidly approach the performance of complete regeneration. Additive interference at each repeater can, however, accumulate adversely in a long chain of repeaters, although an increase in signal power of about 6 dB suffices to make a string of partially regenerative repeaters have an error rate as good as that of a string composed of complete regenerative repeaters. This is also true of repeaters with partial retiming.

6.3 Switching equipment

The various phases of development in p.c.m. switching have been outlined in Section 3.3. This Section will concern itself solely with one practical design embodiment of these developments, to illustrate how the principles can be put into practice.

As already shown in Section 3.3, the only two switching stages to be considered are:
   (i) the switching stage between the subscribers' lines and a p.c.m. highway
   (ii) the switching stage between p.c.m. highways.
These will now be considered in a little more detail.

6.3.1 Switching stage between subscribers' lines and a p.c.m. highway

A p.c.m. highway with 24 channels may serve between 100 and 200 subscribers, depending on their traffic. Therefore the switching stage between the subscribers' lines and a p.c.m. highway has been considered as a concentrator.

In this stage, three types of modulation are present:

   (i) The signal generated by the microphone (or key-set generators) is at voice frequency.

  (ii) The sample gate located in the subscriber equipment produces p.a.m. signals which remain in this form up to the input of the encoder.

 (iii) The encoder generates the p.c.m. codes corresponding to the received p.a.m. signals.

The block diagram (Fig. 33) of this stage shows the three parts of the speech circuit corresponding to these three kinds of modulation.

Subscriber equipment

Each subscriber line, which can be either 4- or 2-wire, is connected to the subscriber equipment. These equipments represent a very substantial part of the total cost of an exchange (nearly 40%), and they include adapting circuits, filters and sampling gates. In the case of a 2-wire line, the adapting circuits must include a hybrid transformer, since the transmitting and receiving paths are separated in the p.c.m. highway.

Various solutions have been envisaged for the realisation of the adapting circuits, and a particularly attractive one uses only semiconductor devices without any coil. Such a solution, in conjunction with RC filters, enables the realisation of the subscriber equipment with chip circuits, this being the most promising way to achieve cost reduction. The problems associated with RC filters have already been mentioned in Section 6.1.1.

The transmit and receive sampling gates are merely transistors used as simple gates. They can be easily integrated into a chip or thin-film circuit.

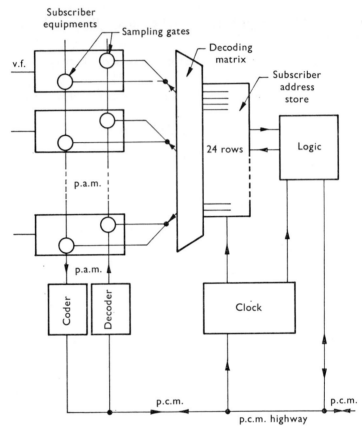

Fig. 33   Typical switching stage between subscribers' lines and a
24-channel p.c.m. highway

Connection with p.a.m. highway

The connection between the subscriber equipment and the p.a.m. highway is performed by the sampling gates. As mentioned above, this switching stage behaves like a concentrator, and this behaviour is obtained through the control of these gates. A store having 24 rows (i.e. one per p.c.m. channel) is associated with the gates. In each row, the number of the subscriber to which the corresponding channel is allocated is written.

The store is read cyclically, and, when a row is read out, the decoding matrix associated with the store sends an opening signal to the sampling gates of the subscriber, thus making the desired connection. Therefore, establishing and releasing a call consists only in writing or erasing the number of the subscriber in the proper place in the store. These operations are performed by a logic circuit which receives the orders it has to carry out from the parent exchange through the p.c.m. junction.

A clock synchronised by the incoming signals from the exchange generates all the timing signals needed by the various circuits.

Connection with p.c.m. highway

The connection between the p.a.m. and p.c.m. highways is, of course, performed through the encoder and the decoder. The use of these devices at the concentrator, and thus the general organisation of this stage, arises from speed and price considerations concerning the encoder and decoder.

6.3.2 Switching stage between p.c.m. multiplex highways

The switching between p.c.m. multiplex highways makes possible the connection between any channel of any highway and any other channel of the same highway or of any other highway. There are therefore two kinds of switching to be performed; namely, switching in time and switching in space. Depending on the speed of the elements used, it is possible to handle the signal corresponding to one or several highways in series or parallel. The descriptions that follow deal with a single 24-channel p.c.m. highway; it is, however, possible to handle, in the same switching unit, 48, 96 or 192 channels.

Storing of speech signals—switching in time

In the exchange, the incoming signals are stored in a fast memory. The signal of the first channel is stored in the first row and so on; the memory therefore comprises 24 rows. The number of bits per row will depend on the number of speech bits per character.

The switching in time (see Fig. 34) is performed by reading out these signals at the time slot defined by the central logic. In order to achieve this, a second memory of 24 rows is associated with the previous one, and the number of an incoming channel is written in each row. This second memory is read cyclically, and when one of its rows is read, the row of the first memory whose number is so obtained is read out too. In this way, the signal of a particular incoming channel is read out at the time slot corresponding to the row number of the

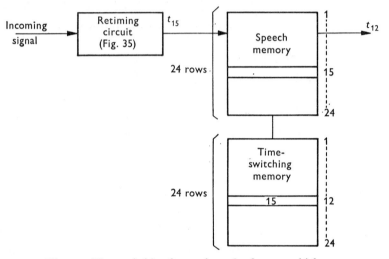

Fig. 34 Time switching for 24 channels of a p.c.m. highway

second memory, this time slot being defined by the logic circuit, in accordance with the call being established. The first memory has been called the speech memory and the second one the time-switching memory. This process suppresses completely the need for any time-slot alignment.

Synchronisation

As already pointed out in Section 3.3.4, one solution for synchronising an integrated p.c.m. network can be attained by adopting a quasisynchronous process, involving retiming of the incoming bit streams from other exchanges, under control of the local-exchange clock. This does not apply to the concentrators, which are, of course, fully synchronised by their own exchange. The basic principles of the quasisynchronous process are as follows.

Upon arrival in an exchange, the signals from a distant exchange are processed in three steps for synchronisation purposes. The first step eliminates jitter, the second staticises the words (channels), and the third compensates for the slight differences in frequency between the clocks of the two exchanges. The first step consists of rephasing

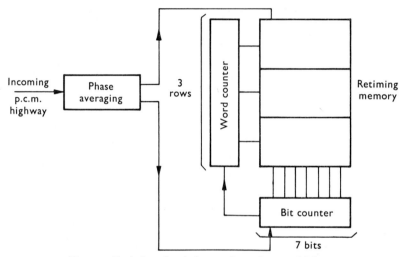

Fig. 35   Retiming circuit for 24-channel p.c.m. highway

only; a circuit including a quartz crystal determines the mean phase of the incoming signal and makes it possible to place the impulses, after reshaping, in their proper place. One rephasing circuit is required for each p.c.m. highway. The second and third steps involve central equipment common to all the highways coming into the exchange, as well as equipment individual to each highway. The second step consists of writing the incoming signals into a small memory (one per incoming highway). This stage is shown in Figs. 35 and 36, and, in this particular instance, it is shown as a 3-row store of 7 bit/ row. In the outline of the exchange organisation on page 97, the description is in terms of an 8 bit/row store (i.e. the channel character consists of eight pulses); the principle, however, is exactly the same in

93

both cases. The writing in the memory is controlled by two counters, one for the row (words) and one for the columns (bits). These counters are controlled by the basic frame of the incoming pulses (after phase averaging). Another counter, counting up to 25 for the highway, gives the number of the incoming channel. Synchronism is obtained if the 25th-channel signal arrives when this counter is at 25. This is

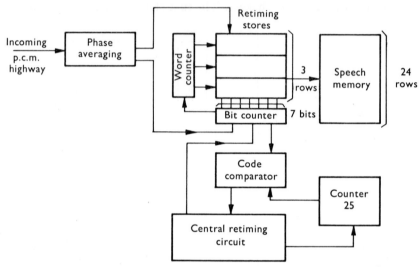

Fig. 36   Combined block diagram of complete retiming arrangements for 25-channel (24 speech + 1 synchronism) p.c.m. highways

shown by a code comparator, which starts the operation of the central common circuit when appropriate.

The common circuit comprises two registers of 8 bits each (Fig. 37). Two successive incoming groups of 8 bits are written into these registers. By parallel decoding, it is possible to determine the place of the synchronisation code, if it exists, and then, after various checks, to send suitable orders to the three counters, to put them in step with the incoming signals. If the synchronisation code does not exist, the signal of register 1 is transferred into register 2 and the next group of eight incoming bits is written in register 1. The comparison is made again, and the cycle is repeated until the correct synchronisation code is found.

94

The third and last step of the synchronisation process consists in writing the 24 incoming words into the speech memory under control of the exchange clock (stability as good as possible and at least one part in 10^6). When the frequencies of the incoming signals and the local clock are exactly the same, word 1 is put into row 1, and so on. But, when there is a slight difference between the two frequencies, it is necessary from time to time to either drop one word (if the local

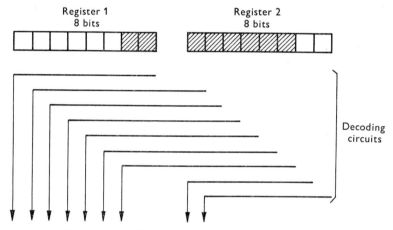

Fig. 37 Central retiming synchronism extraction circuit

clock is too slow) or leave one row blank (if the local clock is too fast). In both cases, a small, but negligible, error will result at readout; e.g. for clock discrepancies of one part in 10^7, there will be one mutilation per channel every 16 min, while, for one part in 10^8, the time period becomes 2 h 40 min.

Space switching

Space switching (Fig. 38) permits interconnection between channels of different highways; this switching is performed by diode gates associated in a matrix. When a connection is established between channel x of incoming highway A on the one hand, and channel y of the outgoing highway B on the other hand, the first operation of switching in time, with the help of the memories, allows the space-switching operation at time slot y. The diode gate located

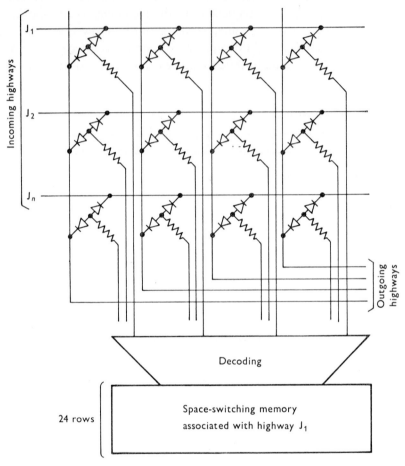

Fig. 38   Space switching between p.c.m. multiplex highways

at the crosspoint between A and B has merely to be opened during time slot y.

This opening is controlled by the space-switching memory associated with A. It comprises 24 rows (one per channel), and the address

96

of the crosspoint to be operated at the time slot corresponding to the reading of this row is written in each row; the memory is read cyclically. It should be emphasised that the establishment of a call consists only in writing the number of the channel and of the highway in the time-switching and space-switching memories, respectively.

Rearrangement

This type of switching makes the so-called rearrangement process particularly easy for completely avoiding internal blocking in the exchange. Blocking arises when many calls are already established and only portions of a free path exist for a new call, without any possibility of connecting them together. In such a case, it is possible to create a path for the new call by changing the paths used for the calls already established. This can be achieved merely by changing the information in the switching memories between two speech-sample time slots.

By virtue of this process, the incoming highways constitute 'perfect groups', and therefore the efficiency of the transmission is increased.

General organisation of the speech network

The two basic types of switching device (time and space) described may be associated in different ways to form the speech network of an exchange. One organisation that is economical in the number of components entailed is described below. The description is based on a channel character of eight bits (i.e. seven speech bits plus one signalling bit). In order to reduce the memory-access and highway-synchronisation circuits, the highways are put into groups of eight highways each.

The eight digits arriving in series at eight successive time slots are registered and afterwards read in parallel. This makes it possible to handle $8 \times 25 = 200$ channels by only one equipment. The equipment processing a group of eight highways each comprising 25 channels (24 speech channels and one synchronisation channel) is shown in Fig. 39.

The eight incoming digits arriving on a highway are first written in

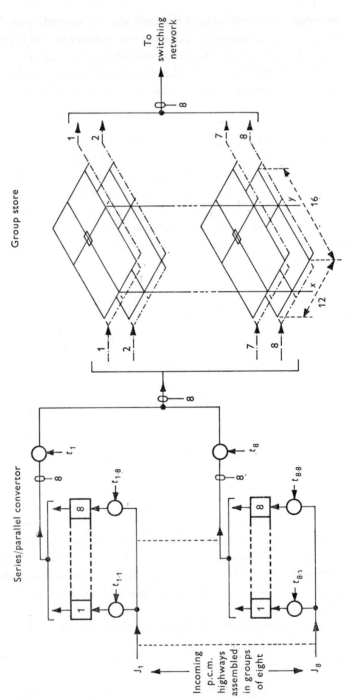

Fig. 39   Equipment for processing a group of eight highways

one row of the small memory of 3 rows used for the synchronisation. This was described on page 93; although, as explained, the circuit operation happens to have been described therein in terms of a 7 bit character rather than the 8 bit signal employed here. These eight digits are afterwards read in parallel, and stored in a speech memory

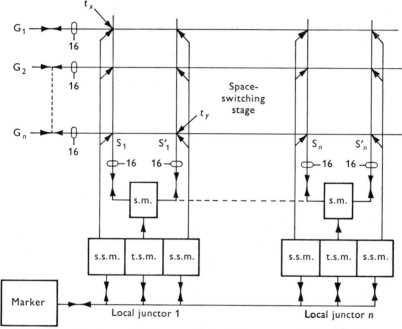

Fig. 40   Complete switching network involving space and time switching

s.s.m. = space-switching memory
t.s.m. = time-switching memory
s.m.   = speech memory

common to the eight junctions of the group. This memory is composed of eight planes (one per digit), each plane comprising $12 \times 16 = 192$ addresses (one per conversation—$192 = 8 \times 24$). The addressing of the 192 conversation signals is operated by the synchronisation circuit.

The switching network is shown in Fig. 40. Here, n groups, each carrying 192 speech channels, are connected at the input of a space-switching stage. Both transmission directions are processed simultaneously, and therefore, with the eight bits being in parallel for each direction, the multiswitch will comprise 16-position crosspoints. The interconnection between two incoming channels is performed through a local junctor, and a speech memory (s.m.) connected to two verticals of the multiswitch is associated with this junctor. For instance, the connection of channel x of group G_1 with channel y of group G_n will be carried out according to the following process:

(i) At the time slot t_x, input G_1 and output S_1 of the multiswitch are connected together, and the signals concerning channel x are transmitted from G_1 to S_1. They are then registered at address x in the memory s.m. of local junctor 1.

(ii) At time slot t_y these same signals are read out from the memory s.m. and transmitted to S_1', which is connected within the multiswitch to input G_n.

(iii) Transmission of the signals from group G_n to group G_1 is carried out according to a similar process through S_1' connected to G_n at time slot t_y, the memory s.m., which operated the switching in time t_y t_x, and the connection between S_1 and G_1 at time slot t_x.

Each local junctor is able to handle 192 different input channels. The control of the multiswitch and the addressing of the signals in the speech memory s.m. are performed in connection with switching memories (time and space). There are two space-switching memories (s.s.m.), which control the connections inside the multiswitch, and a time-switching memory (t.s.m.), which controls the switching in time inside the speech memory. Each of these three memories comprises 192/2 addresses, at which the switching operations to be done at the 192 time slots are registered. Establishing a connection consists in writing in the switching memories the information at the right row, and releasing consists in erasing this information.

The method of rearrangement (see p. 97), consisting in changing, when necessary, the path used by an already established call with a view to establishing a new call, makes it possible to reduce to zero the internal blocking. Therefore, n local junctors are enough to interconnect n incoming groups.

6.3.3 General organisation of a p.c.m. exchange

The control circuit of a p.c.m. exchange takes advantage of the digital form of the speech signals and their multiplexing in time. Owing to the digital form of the speech signal, the control and speech

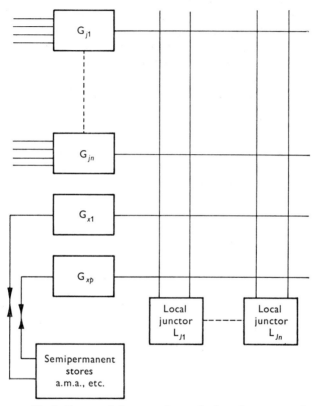

Fig. 41   Block diagram of the general organisation of a p.c.m. exchange

circuits are completely homogenous, and it is even possible to use the same paths for speech and signalling inside the exchange. Furthermore, the marking functions are reduced to writing or erasing digital signals in the memories previously described as a part of the speech circuit. The multiplexing in time makes possible a very simple scanning of all the p.c.m. channels dealt with in a junction group, a local junctor or a concentrator.

These equipments are therefore very simple compared with the corresponding expensive items required for carrying out the same functions in semielectronic exchanges. A typical arrangement is shown in the block diagram of Fig. 41. This shows the speech circuit (i.e. the groups of highways $G_{j1} \ldots G_{jn}$ and the local junctors $L_{J1} \ldots L_{Jn}$, which, with equal numbers of each, gives a nonblocking network) and the control circuit. The latter is divided into several groups G_x, the number of which is determined according to the traffic, each one being capable of handling a certain number of calls.

This organisation gives a satisfactory solution to the reliability problem, since a fault in the G_x group only reduces the service grade.

7 GLOSSARY

Some of the terms used in this monograph are unique to the subject of p.c.m., and, accordingly, they will be unfamiliar to some readers. While every effort has been made to define these terms as they occur in the text, it is felt to be advantageous to give this separate listing of the principal definitions involved. It must be stressed, however, that these are merely the definitions that are pertinent to this monograph, and no claim is made as to their unqualified adoption as accepted terminology. The subject is new, and international bodies such as the CCITT have not yet had time to frame agreed definitions; as and when they do, the definitions listed below may need modifying.

Also included in the list are one or two terms which are not confined to p.c.m. techniques but which may have different connotations in different countries, and which accordingly will benefit by a definition of the context in which they are employed in this monograph.

In alphabetical order, the list is as follows:

Adaptor (or Adapting Circuit)   An element designed to switch a certain number of voice-frequency telephone channels emanating from a non-t.d.m. type of exchange (e.g. an electromechanical exchange) on to a t.d.m. multiplex highway (e.g. a 24-channel p.c.m. junction carrier system).

Character   In p.c.m., a group of $n$ary (usually binary) digits employed to represent a single speech sample; it can include an additional digit over and above the speech digits, to convey, for example, signalling information.

Clock   An equipment providing a time base, used in a transmission system to control the timing of certain functions, such as the control of the duration of signal digits, control of sampling etc.

Codec   A contraction of the two words 'coder' and 'decoder'.

The term may be used to imply the combination of coder and decoder at the same end of a circuit.

Disparity   The excess of marks over spaces in one code character. Thus a zero-disparity code of $2n$ digits has n marks and n spaces, whilst a unit-disparity code (i.e. disparity is ± 1) of $2n-1$ digits has n marks and $n-1$ spaces, or vice versa.

Drift (also jitter and wander)   Terms describing the timing discrepancies between two nominally synchronous timing sources (e.g. between a local exchange clock and a digital bit stream incoming from a distant exchange in an integrated network). Drift is a variation in the nominal clock speeds (i.e. a d.c. shift), jitter is a variation with a very short time constant, and wander is a variation with a long time constant.

Frame (also multiframe and superframe)   The aggregate speech digits (usually binary) and signalling bits resulting from a single sampling of each channel of the total multiplex, together with any additional distinctive synchronising signal (e.g. an extra digit, or an extra character), if employed, to mark the commencement (or termination) of each complete cycle of coded information, are together termed a frame. Where a lower-speed facility (or facilities) is derived by submultiplexing one of the speech channels (or the synchronising channel), the pattern for the lower-speed channels can be made repetitive over a larger number of frames, termed a multiframe. A superframe is defined as the assembly of digits formed by combining a frame of each group of a p.c.m. supergroup, possibly together with a distinctive supergroup synchronising signal.

Group (and supergroup)   These terms have been used for time-division-multiplexed assemblies of channels in the same context as for the accepted conventional f.d.m. connotation. Thus, a t.d.m. group could consist of a 24-channel p.c.m. 'bundle' and a t.d.m. supergroup of, say, 12 t.d.m. groups (i.e. a 288-channel p.c.m. 'bundle').

Highway   A common path over which many separate channels can pass with separation achieved by time division.

Interface   A concept involving the specification of the inter-connection between two equipments having different functions. Such a specification includes the type, quantity and function of the inter-connecting circuits, and the type and form of signals to be interchanged via those circuits.

Jitter   (see *Drift*)

Junction   A link between two exchanges in the same multi-exchange area.

Junctor   A circuit extending between frames of a switching unit and terminating in a switching device on each frame.

Local area   The area in which calls between subscribers are charged at unit fee. According to the subscriber density, such an area may consist of a single exchange serving the whole of the area subscribers, or a number of exchanges each with its own local distribution method and sharing a common numbering scheme (i.e. a simple multioffice area).

Multiframe   (see *Frame*).

Retiming   In an integrated p.c.m. network employing several nominally synchronous clocks (i.e. clock correlation better than one part in 10^6), retiming is the process necessary to control the deviations (i.e. wander and jitter) suffered by a signal timed by a distant clock when it is processed at another exchange under control of a different clock. The term 'retiming' is also used for one of the processes in a regenerative repeater, but here the local clock used for the retiming is directly produced from the timing component inherently present in the incoming line signals.

Slip   When a quasisynchronous mode of operating an integrated network is adopted for dealing with permanent clock differences (i.e. drift), there is occasional slight mutilation of the intelligence, caused by slip, i.e. by a jump (or a pause) in a sequential reading-out process from a retiming store, as dictated by the differential lag (or lead) of the local clock with respect to the distant clock. The frequency of slip is a direct function of the discrepancy in clock speeds.

Superframe (see *Frame*).

Time sampling A process which produces a series of very short pulses of current or voltage, so that the amplitudes of the pulses exactly represent the characteristic ordinates in the original signal wave.

Wander (see *Drift*).

Abbreviations

An alphabetical list of the less-common abbreviations used in this monograph now follows

a.m.a.	automatic message accounting
a.m.i.	alternate mark inversion
ATT	American Telephone and Telegraph Company
CCITT	International Telegraph and Telephone Consultative Committee
EARC	Extraordinary Administrative Radio Conference
e.d.c.	error detection and correction
f.d.m.	frequency-division multiplex
h.s.d.	high-speed data
l.s.d.	low-speed data
m.s.d.	medium-speed data
p.a.b.x.	private automatic branch exchange
p.a.m.	pulse-amplitude modulation
p.c.m.	pulse-code modulation
p.p.m.	pulse-position modulation
p.s.t.	pair-selected ternary
p.t.m.	pulse-time modulation
p.w.m.	pulse-width modulation
s.m.	speech memory
TAT	Transatlantic Telephone Cable
t.d.m.	time-division multiplex
u.d.	unit disparity
v.h.s.d.	very high-speed data

REFERENCES

AARON, M. R. (1962): 'PCM transmission in the exchange plant', *Bell Syst. Tech. J.*, **41**, pp. 99–141

BAGRIT, SIR LEON (1964): British Broadcasting Corporation Reith Lecture

Bell Telephone Laboratories (1964): 'Transmission systems for communications' (Bell Telephone Laboratories) 3rd edn.

British Post Office (1965): Telecommunications Statistics

CAMPBELL, D. R. (1964): 'MESA: A time division multiple access system', Globecom VI Digest of Papers, p. 61

CARTER, R. O. (1965): 'Low-disparity binary coding system', *Electronics Letters*, **1**, pp. 67–8

CATTERMOLE, K. W., *et al.* (1963): 'Experimental PCM transmission for local area telephony', *Elect. Commun.*, **38**, pp. 56–74

CATTERMOLE, K. W. (1964): 'Low-disparity codes and coding for p.c.m.' IEE symposium on transmission aspects of communications networks, pp. 179–82

CCITT (1964*a*): CCITT Blue Book, Vol. 3, question 33/XV

CCITT (1964*b*): CCITT Blue Book, Vol. 4, question 1/XI

CHATELON, A. (1963): 'Application of PCM to an integrated telephone network: Part 2—Transmission and encoding', *Elect. Commun.*, **38**, pp. 32–43

CLEMETT, C. J., *et al.* (1964): 'A six-channel, six-digit t.d.m./p.c.m. system' IEE Symposium on transmission aspects of communications networks, pp. 172–4

COOPER, H. G., *et al.* (1964): 'A high-speed PCM coding tube', *Bell Lab. Record*, **42**, pp. 267–72

CORBATÓ, F. J., *et al.* (1962): 'An experimental time-sharing system', Proceedings of AFIPS joint computer conference, **21**, pp. 335–44

CUTLER, C. C. (1950): US Patent 2605361

DAVIS, C. G. (1962): 'An experimental PCM system for short haul trunks', *Bell Syst. Tech. J.*, **41**, pp. 1–24

DELORAINE, E. M., and REEVES, A. H. (1938): US Patent 2262838

DELORAINE, E. M., VAN MIERLO, S., and DERJAVITCH, B. (1946): French Patent 932140

Extraordinary Administrative Radio Conference, Geneva (1963): Recommendation 4A

FANO, R. M. (1965): 'The MAC system: the computer utility approach', *IEEE Spectrum*, **2**, pp. 56–64

FULTZ, K. E., and PENICK, D. B. (1965): 'The T1 carrier system', *Bell Syst. Tech. J.*, **44**, pp. 1405–51

HEISING, R. A. (1924): US Patent 1655543

JESSOP, A., and CATTERMOLE, K. W. (1964): 'A 23-channel p.c.m. telephone transmission system', IEE symposium on transmission aspects of communications networks, pp. 160–3

KING, B. G., *et al.* (1961): 'Preliminary study of a miniature underwater cable system', *IRE Trans.*, **CS-9**, pp. 159–64

MANN, H., *et al.* (1962): 'A companded coder for an experimental PCM terminal', *Bell Syst. Tech. J.*, **41**, pp. 173–226

MAYO, J. S. (1964): 'An experimental broadband PCM terminal', *Bell Lab. Record*, **42**, pp. 152–7

NEU, W. (1960): 'Some techniques in PCM', *Bull. Schweiz. Elektrotech. Ver.*, **8**, pp. 8–17.

PIERCE, J. R. (1964): 'Telecommunications in 1984—private TV instead of travel', *New Scientist*, (382), pp. 664–5

PURTON, R. F. (1962): 'A survey of telephone speech-signal statistics and their significance in the choice of a p.c.m. companding law', *Proc. IEE*, **109B**, pp. 60–6

REEVES, A. H. (1938): French Patent 852183

REEVES, A. H. (1965): 'PCM—its history, present position and future', *IEEE Spectrum*, **2**, pp. 56–63

SMITH B. (1957): 'Instantaneous companding of quantised signals', *Bell Syst. Tech. J.*, **36**, pp. 653–709

WEED, R. P. (1964): 'Centrex service—a modern PABX concept', *Teleph. Engr. Management*, 15th Oct., pp. 27–32

WALKER, E., and DUERDOTH, W. T. (1964): 'Trunking and traffic principles of a p.c.m. telephone exchange', *Proc. IEE*, **111**, pp. 1976–80

INDEX